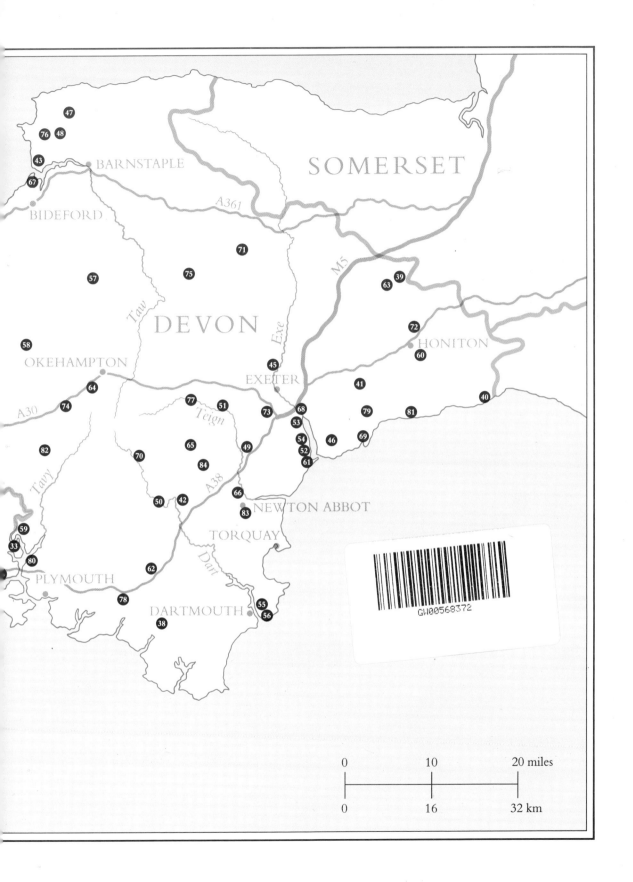

SOMERSET

BARNSTAPLE

A361

BIDEFORD

DEVON

Taw

Exe

M5

OKEHAMPTON

HONITON

A30

Teign

EXETER

A38

NEWTON ABBOT

Tavy

TORQUAY

PLYMOUTH

Dart

DARTMOUTH

47

76 48

43

67

71

75

57

63 39

72

60

58

45

64

74

77 51

73

68

41

82

70

65

49

53

79

81

54

46

69

52

84

61

50 42

66

83

59

33

80

62

78

55

56

38

GW00568372

| 0 | 10 | 20 miles |
| 0 | 16 | 32 km |

WEST
COUNTRY
WILDLIFE

WEST COUNTRY WILDLIFE

A Naturalist's Year in Devon and Cornwall

KELVIN BOOT

ELAINE FRANKS

GEORGE
PHILIP

First published in 1992 by George Philip Limited
59 Grosvenor Street, London W1X 9DA

British Library Cataloguing in Publication Data

Boot, Kelvin
    West Country Wildlife
    I. Title   II. Franks, Elaine
    574.9423

ISBN 0–540–01261–0

Design Louise Dick
Typeset by Keyspools Ltd,
Golborne, Warrington, Lancs.
Printed in Hong Kong

CONTENTS

THE
REGION

The West Country – the triangle of land made up by Devon and Cornwall – is a unique area for naturalists, rich in habitats and species. Surrounded by sea on two of its sides, its varying aspects and landscapes harbour a wealth of wildlife throughout the year.

Climatically the region is warmer than most of Britain, and some parts of Cornwall especially have more in common with the Mediterranean. Seasonally the West Country does not usually show the extremes of other parts of Britain and it can be difficult to draw lines between autumn and winter, spring and summer. Many plants flower much earlier and have a longer season. Likewise 'cold-blooded' animals reliant upon the heat of the sun for their activities, or those which in other parts of the country hibernate, in some years can be seen out and about at almost any time.

Ecologically the West Country is perhaps the most varied region of the British Isles, and most habitat types can be found within its borders. From the muddy, sandy and rocky shores which make up the hundreds of miles of coastline, through the unique ancient Culm Grasslands, delightful wooded valleys and sun-blasted heaths, to the exposed moorlands and the tops of the stark granite tors, the West Country presents a multi-faceted display of nature. Underlying this variety are the rocks which make up the diverse landscape, affect the weather patterns and give rise to the soils which are in turn the foundation of our wildlife.

The oldest rocks of the area are those of The Lizard. Pre-Cambrian in age, they are formed of a mixture of rocks which have originated or been transformed by igneous activity. Metamorphic rocks, gneisses, schists and serpentines each contain their own particular minerals, which concentrate various elements in the soil and result in some interesting plant life. Granites, basalts and dolerites add to the variety and this curious assemblage of rock types, many of which are beautifully exposed along the cliffs, makes The Lizard a paradise for the geologist as well as the botanist.

Much of the two counties is underlain by rocks of the period of geological time which earns its name throughout the world from the county where it was

• *A young sow is wary as she emerges from the sett*

first described in detail – the Devonian. Just before the Devonian started, large earth movements raised a land mass to the north of the region. This arid land was drained by rivers into a sea-filled basin which covered much of Devon and Cornwall around 400 million years ago. This basin formed a natural collecting point for a huge amount of sediments of one sort or another. Pressure and heat, which turn muds and sands into shales and sandstones, produced the rocks we

see today. The gritty deposits which form the non-granite moorland of Exmoor owe their origin to this prehistoric desert landscape. In some parts of the Devonian Period, sea coral thrived and the reefs can be seen today as the Devonian Limestones of South Devon, for example around Torquay. These limestones have a unique flora, and their caves are a sanctuary for some of Britain's rarest bats.

A calm day on the North Cornish coast •

Buzzard
Nest

Red Deer Stag

Bilberry

Buzzard

Ling

Bell
Heather

Cross-leaved
Heath

Much of Mid and North Devon and North-East Cornwall rests on rocks of the Carboniferous Period. These are locally known as the Culm Measures, a name which may refer to the knotted appearance of some of the shales, limestones and siltstones or even to the thin coal beds which occur now and again. Very hard rocks called cherts are the result of volcanic activity. The Culm Measures often result in poorly drained soil and it is to this bedrock that the unique Culm Grasslands and the rolling 'whaleback' landscape of much of the region owe their origin.

Towards the end of the Carboniferous Period earth movements took place on a tremendous scale and one result was the emplacement of the series of granite bosses which now dominate both Devon and Cornwall. Experts differ as to just how these huge masses of granite originated. Some maintain that they were formed in place by the melting of a mixture of rocks which already existed; others suggest that the granite was pushed into place as molten rock from within the earth's crust. Whichever is the case (and it was most likely a combination of the two), it is agreed that when first formed the granite was underground and has since been exposed by erosion. Also the granites are no longer thought of as distinct bodies of rock, but as the tips of a single 'iceberg' of granite which underlies the whole region. Each tip now forms an area of resistant, high land. The Dartmoor Granite and Bodmin are perhaps the largest and best known, but there are others at St Austell, Carnmenellis, Land's End and the Scillies.

This convulsion of the earth, which took place some 280 million years ago, produced many fascinating landscape features. The granite uplands are responsible for most of the rivers which flow in the area, and themselves produce an interesting series of wildlife habitats. Since the tors are the result of weathering at a later date in geological time, many of them are surrounded by extensive slopes consisting of broken blocks of granite – the clitter slopes. Throughout the period of emplacement of the granite and for a long time afterwards, lesser activity took place which itself produced a variety of intrusions both above and below ground. Volcanic activity affected much of the region and evidence of local lava flows and minor intrusions as well as faulting can be seen in many places.

Immediately after this period of igneous and earth-moving activity much of the West Country was raised from the sea. The then equator is thought to have been very close and desert conditions prevailed over much of the region. Evidence for this can be seen along the shoreline today, particularly around Budleigh Salterton, with fossil sand dunes, mudcracks, gypsum deposits and wind-faceted pebbles all bearing witness to the arid conditions in which they were formed. River channels also existed and there is even evidence of overflowing banks in some places. On land the early reptiles were just getting ready for their evolutionary spurt which would make them dinosaurs, the rulers of the earth. The sands and muds of this formation of rock lend the rich red colour to the soil for which Devon is justly famous. Pebble Beds in East Devon underlie some of the few remaining heathlands and the sandstones along the coast, between Paignton and Seaton, supply the material for the sandy beaches. The cliffs themselves offer many perches for a variety of seabirds and where they reach the sea are easily eroded by it to form some of the best rockpools in the area.

Tropical seas encroached upon this land mass, laying down the limestones and shales of the Jurassic Period. While much of this cover has since been eroded or covered by later sediments, these fossil-rich rocks can still be found exposed in the extreme east of Devon. Along the coast beyond Seaton these rocks and those of the next period, the Cretaceous, slump into a jumble which provides the setting for some of the most dramatic walking country in the area: the Undercliffs, a series of almost jungle-like covered land slips. The lime-rich chalks themselves produce impressive headlands and unique clifftop grasslands, while remnant Cretaceous deposits are also found further west in Devon. Here the hills of Little and Great Haldon are composed of greensand and the soil is full of flints. Heathland predominates, while forestry thrives.

• *Rough Tor, Bodmin*

Tertiary deposits are very limited, but do produce some interesting habitats. The Tertiary Period saw a warm climate with high rainfall, a combination with great erosive powers. Decaying feldspar minerals from the granite were carried into huge lakes and collected as the muds which are now exploited as ball clays in the areas around Bovey Tracey and Petrockstowe. Much of the area is heathy and a series of ponds valuable for wildlife have formed in abandoned workings. The china clays of Cornwall have also produced some interesting stretches of fresh water, although they are less prolific in wildlife because they tend to be deeper. The spoil heaps produced are an eye-catching, if barren, feature.

Erosion continued during the next period, the Quaternary, when many of the caves were hollowed out, the tors continued to be eroded and the Ice Ages came and went. During the colder periods, the glacial water levels dropped and exposed a 'land bridge' to continental Europe, over which animals were free to come and go. Migrations of different animals would have been triggered by changes in climate. After the last cold spell the sea rose again, and Britain became an island once more: the bridge was cut off forever. Evidence of a variety of sea-level changes can be seen along much of the coast. Raised beaches

indicate a sea-level higher than at present, while drowned forests, occasionally exposed at low tides in Torbay and around the Hayle Estuary among other places, indicate a much lower sea-level than we see today.

Birds, butterflies and other flying creatures could, of course, still make the journey across the channel, but Britain as an island was essentially cut off from the flora and fauna which flourished in Europe. It is at this point, about 4500 years ago, that the wildlife we see today became established. When climatic changes have taken place the fortunes of our native plants and animals have waxed and waned in accord with natural events.

• *Heathland, near Woodbury, Exeter*

Human settlement became established in the West Country in around 4000 BC, and it is arguable that early man had an effect on some of the animals with which he competed for food and shelter. There is no doubt that animals were hunted for food, clothing and as a source of tools and weapons. But it is not certain that early man, who no doubt should be thought of as living in a state of balance with nature, was ever totally responsible for the extinction of some of the wonderful beasts which inhabited our land. By 500 BC, however, with the spread of 'civilisation' and the exploitation of nature, man had upset a delicate balance, which will never be regained, no matter what we do. Vast tracts of

forest continue to be devastated to provide timber or space for agriculture, so that only a fraction of our original woodland remains, and many animals have been mercilessly persecuted in the name of grain and game preservation. Gone from Britain are the bears, wolves, beaver and wild boar. Gone from the West Country are the pine martens, polecats and wild cats. Alien animals destructive to our native fauna and flora have been introduced with little thought for the consequences. And now we are suffering the legacy of powerful chemicals, liberally applied to the land in the name of efficiency or progress.

The warm climate prevailing in Devon and Cornwall today needs little introduction, since many thousands of holidaymakers who visit each year are testimony enough. The higher areas, centred around the granite moorlands, attract a high rainfall which ensures an adequate supply of river waters to the low lands into which they drain. This combination of warmth and moisture

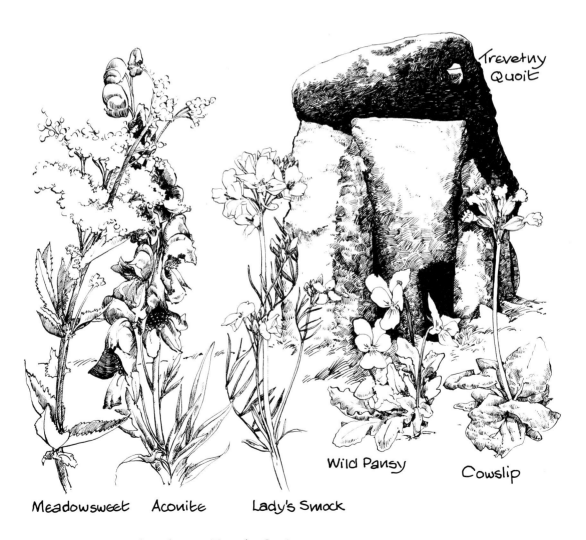

Trevethy Quoit

Wild Pansy

Cowslip

Meadowsweet   Aconite   Lady's Smock

16   • *Meadow plants at Trevethy Quoit*

• *Old farm buildings on the Two Moors Way*

ensures that many plants and the animals which depend on them survive in the West Country while elsewhere in Britain they are absent or rare. Devon boasts Britain's warmest nature reserve at Dawlish Warren, and The Lizard and Land's End show striking similarities of flora with that of the Mediterranean. But the West Country has its own extremes of climate. Stunted and wind-sculpted trees, sometimes well inland, are evidence of the strong winds which come in from the sea and the high tors of the granite moorlands can be stark and cold places, with the spring coming late and the autumn early.

17

SPRING

S pring comes early to most parts of the West Country; indeed for many animals and some of the plants winter makes hardly any difference as the climate is so mild. There is, however, a time when nature really wakes up and gets ready for the productive seasons to come. The chill leaves the earth and the plants put on spurts of growth. Insects roused from their slumbers rise into the air and mammals and birds begin the business of finding mates and establishing territories before bringing their families into the world. Of all habitats the woodlands seem to come alive the most rapidly. Trees that are stark and bare through the darker months of winter open their buds, a sign of the dense green canopies to come.

Numerous areas of woodland are found in the hidden valleys or combes in the West Country. Having defeated the plough or grazing animals, they are homes to a huge variety of animals and plants. These 'valley woodlands' may tantalize the visitor when they are suddenly revealed by a fortuitous bend in the road, and one of the great pleasures of driving in this part of the world is when the road skirts the edge of one of these woodlands giving a bird's-eye view right down into the woods. Fortunately there are some large tracts of valley woodland which, while open to the public, still retain a certain 'wildness' and provide a home for a huge and fascinating selection of animals and plants. The valleys of the Dart, Teign, Exe, Bovey and Taw/Torridge in Devon and the Fal, Fowey and Helston rivers in Cornwall all have fine woods, and Lanhydrock in Cornwall and Yarner Wood in Devon are worth a visit. Patchy woodland also exists in many of the hidden combes that conceal smaller rivers, and the large estates have retained much of their tree cover. The Devon Wildlife Trust Nature Reserve at Dunsford follows the north bank of the River Teign for about four miles and the combination of steep valley, flood plain and the River Teign itself provide a variety of habitats including woodland, scrub, heath-covered, rocky slopes and open grassland.

Many of the West Country's woodlands are regarded as semi-natural: although managed as a resource they are largely left to their own devices for much of the year. The traditional management technique of coppicing,

• *Alert kingfisher on the Little Dart, Mid Devon*

however, has given Dunsford and Meadhaydown Woods as well as other woodlands, their character as well as providing much of their current interest. Oak and hazel were long regarded as valuable trees and both were harvested by coppicing in many West Country woods. The trees were cut down to within a few inches of the ground, the cut being made at a slight angle to allow run-off and prevent rotting of the remaining stump or 'stool'. New growth sprang up in the form of easily accessible and relatively straight branches which were cut for hurdle-making and other uses. The advantage to wildlife was that areas of woodland floor were opened up to the light, encouraging growth of a diverse ground flora. Today, little coppicing is carried out, the policy being to encourage full growth to high woodland – the natural development for a

20   • *Water vole and marsh marigold on a North Devon river*

habitat such as this. There is however, plenty of evidence for former management by coppicing and large trees sprouting from a very low stool can be seen growing among stands of birch and ash which have been left to develop naturally. Other trees of the shrub layer are blackthorn, crab apple, hawthorn, alder buckthorn and spindle.

Generally speaking, woodlands harbour more wildlife than almost any other habitat and a spring walk will be amply rewarded. Long before the buds on the trees open into full leaf and shade the woodland floor, the smaller flowers are growing and producing blooms to catch the first pollinators of the year. Among the earliest flowers to erupt from the sanctuary of the earth are those which have husbanded their resources from the previous growing season.

Sparkling golden celandines are the most striking against the browns and greens of the ground. They may look like buttercups, but a closer investigation will reveal that they have between eight and twelve petals as opposed to the normal five of the buttercup family. The name celandine comes from an ancient Greek word meaning swallow, and the flowers are supposed to herald the arrival of the bird. In the West Country they bloom over a long period and may well coincide with swallows, but the flower can appear very early in the

Dog Violet

Bluebell   Ramsons   Primrose

• *Woodland flowers near Witheridge on the Two Moors Way*

spring. The celandine gets off to a good start as soon as the weather warms even slightly, and this is due to the fact that they have a good reserve of food below ground in the form of a root tuber.

Amongst the celandines may be found another flower with a name of Greek origin – the wood anemone or wind flower, from the Greek *anemos* meaning 'wind' – whose delicate white flowers bend at the slightest breeze. Like the celandine it also has an underground cache of food, but this time in the form of a rhizome. The primrose, one of the most familiar of spring flowers, relies on a root stock for its initial spurt of growth and before long the woodland floor is carpeted with the pale-yellow blooms peaking out from the leaf litter of the previous autumn, the golden browns, yellows and greens producing a pleasing mosaic. The name primrose alludes to its early flowering, literally meaning 'first rose', and the Latin name of Primula is a shortened form of the French 'primeverole' – the first flower of spring. April 19th is designated Primrose Day in honour of the Victorian prime minister Benjamin Disraeli, whose favourite flower it was – a fact recognised by the Queen, who would often send him gifts of primroses.

Primroses bear a closer look for it will be found that there are two different sorts of flower. In the one type the style is above the anthers – pin eyed; in the second type the style is below the anthers – thrum eyed. This is an elaborate mechanism for ensuring that the flowers are cross-pollinated but it is probably just as well that the primrose can also reproduce vegetatively, for some populations are made up of only one type and many flowers are in bloom before the insects they would otherwise rely upon for pollination have emerged in any numbers. Some primrose plants have been known to live for twenty years or more.

As spring progresses it seems that the early yellow and white flowers give way to blues and purples. The anemones, celandines and primroses cease flowering and make way for carpets of bluebells and delicate violets. This sequence of colours is only an appearance, for it is not long before the ramsons, with their pungent garlicky scent, delight both the eye and nose, their white blooms so thick in places that you might think that there had been an overnight snowfall, and the nodding golden heads of the wild daffodils take over. One of the strangest plants of the spring woods is 'Lords and Ladies', with its blotched dark-green leaves and its poker-like flower. This is one of the flycatchers; smaller diptera are lured by the scent and become trapped by the downward-pointing hairs at the base, where the female flowers are to be found. The flies carry pollen from male flowers with which the females can be fertilised. Only when all the flowers have received their quota does the plant relinquish its hold on its captives. The hairs die back and the flies crawl out, brushing against the male flowers and acquiring more pollen on the way. It seems that these flies never learn, but go off in search of other plants where once more they become temporary captives.

Minnow

Alder

Otter

Dipper

Blackthorn
and Lichens

While the carpet layer of the woodland has been active the other plants have begun to catch up. On the trees the leaves have begun to unfurl and the plants of summer have grown tall. The time of the lowly plants is almost at an end. Violets and primroses enlarge their leaves in an effort to catch as much of the sun as possible before they are completely shaded out and photosynthesis slows down. Food is produced and transported to whatever storage organ nature has dictated each plant should use, to ensure that come the next spring they are ready and waiting to push forth green shoots to catch the spring sunshine.

From the earliest days of spring the hazel has been producing its catkins. Indeed hazel can be regarded as the first sign of spring, if not of settled weather, for it is often in flower in February. The long yellow catkins are the male flowers and if you look closely at the twigs you will find the smaller reddish female flowers. Such early flowering and so much pollen at the same time might seem risky or wasteful, but the hazel is a plant which is pollinated by the wind. This is not as accurate a method as using an insect; hence the amount of pollen which must be produced, giving the tree its yellow colour at this time of year. A covering of leaves would only inhibit dispersal of the pollen, so flowering takes place before the leaves have unfurled. The pendulous catkins of the birch also appear early, and these are soon followed by silver-furred pussy willows.

Thousands of years ago much of the West Country would have been covered with a dense blanket of woodland, dominated by oaks. It is difficult to imagine Dartmoor or the rolling farmlands of the region cloaked in forest, but the aspect of the land was very different then to what we see today. Large stands of oak woodland are now a rarity and many a favourite 'forest' is more the result of human interference than a product of natural development. Many are the result of plantings to redress the balance of lost woodlands felled for fuel, ship-building, and increasingly at the demands of agriculture. Even so, the West Country is fortunate in having some of the few remaining examples of truly natural woodland to be found in Britain or indeed of any habitat which has not been created as a by-product of human progress. Dartmoor has some of the best-known examples: Piles Copse, Black Tor Copse and, perhaps most famous of all, Wistman's Wood. Why these isolated and small remnants have withstood the rigours of human demand for wood and land remains a mystery, but it is probably a result of inaccessibility and rough terrain.

Clinging to a steep valleyside just a few miles from the road to Two Bridges, Wistman's Wood is straight out of a fairy tale. If elves and goblins exist anywhere, it is here that they thrive: even the oaks are of the pedunculate variety, the long-stalked acorn cups looking remarkably like elvish pipes. The name itself is shrouded in mystery and may refer to the Devil – the Wistman. What makes Wistman's Wood so very different is the way that the trees have grown among the clitter to produce a bonsai woodland. Full-grown oaks may only be 4.5 m or so in height, their roots tightly bound by the granite boulders: they grow as they can, between, over and around the very rocks which

• River valley between Barnstaple and Tiverton

sheltered the first shoots from the scything winds of the moor. These gnarled and twisted oaks are of great antiquity – some of them are thought to be five hundred years old – but their girth rarely exceeds 45 cm and they never reach anything approaching the full height of a normal oak. The atmosphere is especially eerie when swirling Dartmoor mists shroud the wood.

Ecologically Wistman's Wood provides us with a fascinating glimpse into the past. Was this truly what the rest of our landscape looked like when bears and wolves roamed the two counties of Devon and Cornwall? The value of the wood is recognised by the fact that it has been designated as a Forest Nature Reserve and is under the care of English Nature. Such a gem is under constant threat and visitors are asked to keep to the winding footpath which traverses the wood and from which everything can be seen. A good part of the woodland has been fenced off to study natural regeneration, when livestock and people are barred from entry.

From a distance Wistman's Wood can look most unpromising, a trick of the varying Dartmoor light which gives the wood a greyish lichen colour one day

Wistman's Wood, Dartmoor • 27

BOUNDARIES

The deep lanes, high hedgebanks and walls which mark the fields of Devon and Cornwall are among the most noticeable features to the visitor. For the naturalist they provide a unique series of linear habitats which give shelter to a wealth of plants and animals. The more sheltered walls are soon taken over by the plants of the sheltered valleys, and rapidly become festooned with mosses, lichens and ferns, welcome patches of green against the greys and browns of the stone. The hart's tongue and the delicate maidenhair spleenwort are among the more common species. Shade-loving plants such as the arum lily thrive in the darkness at the base of hedges, where its bizarre leafy spathe envelopes the poker-like flower head. Where this is constricted a circle of hairs allows insects in to pick up pollen from the male flowers. Once the pollen has been dropped the hairs shrivel and the insect escapes to visit another flower where it will almost certainly leave some pollen behind to fertilise the female flowers and allow the bright red berries to develop.

Carn Euny Well

Maidenhair Spleenwort

Cuckoo Pint

quite unlike the brilliant green oasis of the next. The canopy close to ground level, the dense foliage and the natural high rainfall ensure that this wood is a humid place. Thus, on a warm day, it provides a welcoming cool stillness from the sun or the winds of the more exposed surrounding moorland. The high humidity also ensures that a good growth of vegetation is found within the wood itself and it has been said that everything which grows on the woodland floor is to be found growing on the trees themselves. It is these epiphytic plants which make Wistman's one of the truly wonderful sites of the West Country. Boulder and tree alike are festooned with mosses and lichens. Ferns sprout from almost every junction of limb and trunk and ivy grasps its way along the ground and up the deformed oaks, with climbing honeysuckle adding a splash of colour and delightful scent. Thick mats of whortleberry cover the branches and it is often difficult to determine where ground stops and tree starts. The closed-off area gives some indication of what a jungle Wistman's Wood can be without the tramping feet of humans and the rasping teeth of sheep and ponies.

Progress through the wood is now much easier than it was even a few years ago, but care needs to be taken for the moss-covered boulders are slippery when wet. The ground layer of the wood, where it can be distinguished, holds most of the plants familiar to oak woodland. Particularly noticeable are the dense growth of woodrush, the pretty four-petalled, yellow tormentil, fragrant herb Robert and the ubiquitous foxglove.

The damp ground is an ideal habitat for frogs and you need to watch where you are stepping as they can amount to almost a plague in some years, the shelter of the wood providing them with the humidity they require to emerge during the daylight. Adders also thrive in the wood, especially around its edges, and a carelessly placed hand can result in a bite. Usually, however, these fairly shy snakes stay well out of the way of stumbling humans, and are frightened by their noisy approach.

The surrounding moorland is always ready to encroach, as is indicated by the strong growths of bracken at the woodland edge. Many bird species from the surrounding area find a resting place amongst the branches of the trees and it is especially worth looking out for birds of prey. The woods themselves, although small in extent, provide a home for a variety of species, mostly familiar birds like the blue tit, chaffinch and robin, and the distinctive call of the cuckoo is often heard as the birds proclaim their territories, beckon a mate and invade the nests of small birds. The high altitude of the relict oaks means that spring comes later to this particular woodland than to other parts of the West Country, sometimes giving the naturalist a second chance to see the annual burgeoning of nature.

Resident animals and plants can take advantage of an early spring in order to get started on the business of growing or nesting, flowering or egg laying. Spring can suddenly become very hectic as the early-nesting birds go about their business of setting up territories, finding a mate, producing their young and feeding them. A good early start can mean a second or third brood, ensuring that the chances of survival of at least some of their offspring are high. Many resident birds will nest before the end of March, taking a chance on the weather. The crossbill is perhaps the earliest nester although this bird is far from common in the area. It has been known to nest in the plantations on the East Devon Commons and at Great Haldon near Exeter in Devon, and in these areas the birds are usually somewhat gregarious. There is no evidence to suggest that they have bred in Cornwall. The crossbill is a superb example of nature's inventiveness; the characteristic bill from which the bird is named is a wonderful adaption for extracting the seeds from pine cones and the bird may be found in areas where pine trees grow. Most of the crossbills seen in Britain are migrants which come in during the summer months. Some of these stay on during the winter and start to lay their eggs in late January or February.

The stately heron, the sentinel of even the smallest waterways, is also an early breeder and the first good weather during February is a signal for this bird to start spring cleaning and get the nest in order. Tall, gangly herons appear quite incongruous as they balance precariously in the tree tops or alight on a branch with some critical twig for the untidy structures to which they will soon entrust their eggs. Precarious though these arboreal nest sites might be they are much safer than nesting on the ground among the diminishing reed beds and marshes. Heronries are found in both Devon and Cornwall usually where secluded tall trees and estuarine waters are close together although they can be found inland. Near Jamaica Inn on Bodmin Moor is one such place. The largest heronry in the West Country is in the grounds of Powderham Castle along the Exe Estuary, but even this has only about thirty nests. In Cornwall the colonies are much smaller and rarely achieve double figures, that on the Camel Estuary being among the largest.

The middle of February also sees the largest crow laying its eggs. Ravens are huge birds and are widespread nesters in Devon and Cornwall, where rugged seacliffs, inland rocky outcrops and woodlands all provide them with secure sites. Their laborious style of flight, harsh cronking call and large size all serve to distinguish them from their smaller cousins, the rooks and crows.

February is also the month to watch plump dippers as they build their nests in some crevice along the river bank or under a bridge on some secluded ledge. The dipper is the one bird which I always associate with the fast-moving rivers of the West Country. Wherever the water is clear and clean, rock strewn and gravelly-bottomed, the dipper is to be found. More often than not the dipper streaks upriver on whirring wings, its brown back and white chest providing immediate identification. Patience will be rewarded if you settle yourself down and wait for the bird's return, for it is most likely that you have disturbed it from its favourite diving platform. Soon the dipper is back and after bobbing up and down a little, which may explain its name, it dives into the water, another possible explanation for its name. Beneath the surface the wings are

Heron on a cold afternoon on the River Waldon near Bradworthy •

spread and the bird is held down by the force of the current flowing over its tilted body; it almost walks on the riverbed in search of the water insects which are its food. If you watch carefully you will soon see the bird pop up at some point downstream and leave the water to rest on a rocky islet. From here it may perhaps enter the water again and again or float with the current and 'duck dive' from the surface.

Nesting is soon taken up by more familiar birds. The song thrush, which has been proclaiming the coming of spring in its liquid call for weeks, joins in at the end of February. So, too, does the tawny owl as if knowing that the vegetation will soon be too tall for nocturnal hunting among the trees and that prey will be hidden. In gardens the invisible lines which mark territories are being fought over by blackbirds and robins. Robins are among the most territorial of birds and are particularly aggressive when the breeding season is at its height. Such is their possessiveness at this time of year that they even end up fighting themselves, or at least their own reflections in windows and car hubcaps and wing mirrors. Robins have been known to pursue a car until it is out of their territory and even red pullover-wearers have been known to bear the brunt of their aggression.

By the time many of these birds have built their nests and raised the first clutch of youngsters, the woods, heaths, moors and hedgerows are starting to come alive with sounds which have not been heard since the previous summer. In mid-March the migrant birds start arriving. One of the first sounds to be heard is the onomatopoeic call of the chiffchaff which serves to distinguish it from the very similar-looking willow warbler, a bird which arrives in this country a couple of weeks later. Confusion can arise in areas where chiffchaffs overwinter, as they are known to do in some parts of the West Country. Both of these birds prefer woodland and can be found in a wide variety of habitats where trees grow.

It is often said that one swallow does not make a summer and certainly some of the earlier records for this species show that the arrival of swallows is no indication of warmer weather. In Devon and Cornwall swallows have been spotted as prematurely as late February, but the first of the swallow-like birds to arrive in any numbers are the sand martins. Around the middle of March the acrobatic, brown-feathered martins are to be seen around waterways and marshy areas where there are at least some insects to satisfy the hunger they have generated on their long flights and there are banks with holes for nesting in. Sand martins are notoriously finicky and will abandon a site for no apparent reason, only to return to it a few years later. Quarries in the sand of East Devon are an alternative to river banks and in Cornwall these birds have even nested in the spoil heaps from mineral workings. A couple of weeks later the flocks of twisting and turning sand martins seem to grow as they are joined by house martins, easily distinguished by their white rumps. Finally the swallows arrive, streaking through the air with their tails streaming behind them.

• *Less wary than their elders, a pair of young badgers leave the sett before dusk*

For many people the sound of the first cuckoo heralds the start of spring. The rarities committees of the national and county bird watching organisations however, no longer accept the sound without a sighting, and even a sighting should be given a second look for the cuckoo, which is a bird of many habitats, can look surprisingly like the ubiquitous sparrowhawk. In fact it was widely accepted before migration was fully understood that cuckoos actually turned into hawks for the winter. Meadow pipit, reed warbler, dunnock, robin, sedge warbler and pied wagtail are the chief victims of the cuckoo's parasitic egg-laying, but it is not restricted to these species and about fifty different types of birds have been the recipients of its eggs. Its lack of parental responsibility means that once its twelve or so eggs are laid the cuckoo leaves us. The old rhyme sums up the life of the cuckoo pretty well; even the loud cuckooing tails off after the initial period of egg-laying:

In April come she will;
In May he sings all day;
In June he alters his tune;
In July he prepares to fly;
In August go he must.

Not only has the cuckoo etched out a unique lifestyle in Britain but it is also notable for cornering the market in a particular food source. The large caterpillars of moths such as the drinker would provide a tasty morsel for any bird but for the fact that they are clothed in a dense covering of irritating hairs. However, this does not bother cuckoos and they regularly feed on these caterpillars which have spent the winter months in hibernation and emerge to pupate. Cuckoos can be heard in most habitats and are widespread throughout the West Country but they can be quite elusive. I have always had my best sightings near reed beds and up on the open moorlands where trees are few and far between; it becomes a simple matter to predict where the cuckoo will come to rest. They can also be spotted mating just before dusk near overgrown quarries filled with water, where they attract the attention of small birds in the vicinity which rise to mob them.

The wryneck arrives at about the same time as the cuckoo and so is often given the name of cuckoo's mate. This bird is a rare visitor which turns up from time to time and has bred in Devon. In most years a few are seen in deciduous woodlands, where unlike its close relatives, the woodpeckers, it picks insects off the surface of the bark rather than boring into trees for them.

Throughout the early spring the woodlands gain a little more life each day as more and more visiting birds move in, establish territories and set up home. Nesting and egg-laying begin apace and by the end of April most of the birds are about the business of feeding young. An early start is necessary to appreciate fully the admixture of voices which gradually build to the full chorus – a crescendo of sounds which stretches the skill and hearing of birdwatchers. Often this starts with the blackbird half an hour or so before sunrise. Soon the voice of the song thrush is added to fluid duet while the wood pigeon seems to keep time with its deeper notes in the background. The raucous pheasant keeps the offbeat, the whole chorus is joined by the beautiful sound of the willow warbler and eventually by the crazed piccolo of the diminutive wren – the smallest bird with the loudest voice.

Eventually all the migrants have selected their homes and life really begins. Nesting and egg-laying are followed by a period of intense activity as the parents strive to keep their young and themselves well supplied with food. Much of this is in the form of insects, especially caterpillars, and the insectivorous birds are to be seen on moorland and heath, woodland and hedgerow with their bills full of soft juicy prey.

Being 'cold-blooded' creatures, insects are not really active until the weather is relatively settled and the frosts are far behind. Eggs hatch, caterpillars emerge, pupae erupt into adulthood and the hibernating imagos stretch their wings as spring advances. Just as one swallow does not make a summer so one butterfly does not make a spring, but there can be no more beautiful a sight than that of a brimstone butterfly flitting from the early primrose blooms on a warm day in spring. Aptly named, the brimstone is a sulphur or butter yellow in colour and is quite unlike any of the other butterflies which might be seen at this time of year. The adult butterfly hibernates through the colder spells of winter. Eager to make a start at the first hint of warm weather, however, it might be seen on

• *Rooks and brimstone butterfly on lady's smock in grassland near Land's End*

any sunny day in winter. Not only is it distinguished by being one of the first butterflies of the year it is also thought to be responsible for the very name butterfly itself. Originally this lepidopteran was known, because of its colour, as the butter-coloured fly, a title which became shortened to butterfly.

Another early butterfly may be the small tortoiseshell, roused from its slumbers to take advantage of the first spell of warm weather. The ragged-winged comma may also be seen very early in the year, having also hibernated throughout the winter. When at rest in a hollow tree the dark underside of the wings with their characteristic 'commas' make them difficult to detect among the other dead leaves of winter. As the season progresses more and more species

AYLESBEARE POND

During late spring, life around the pond is in full swing and much of this can be observed from the banks. In the shallower, warmer waters, near the edge, the common or smooth newts are indulging in their fascinating mating dances, where the male curves his body into a U-shape and approaches the waiting female, his body literally quivering with anticipation. For the dragonflies and damselflies a watery youth of three years or so ends early one late spring morning when they clamber out of the water and up the stem of a water plant. With a split of its skin the ugly larva is transformed into a flying jewel.

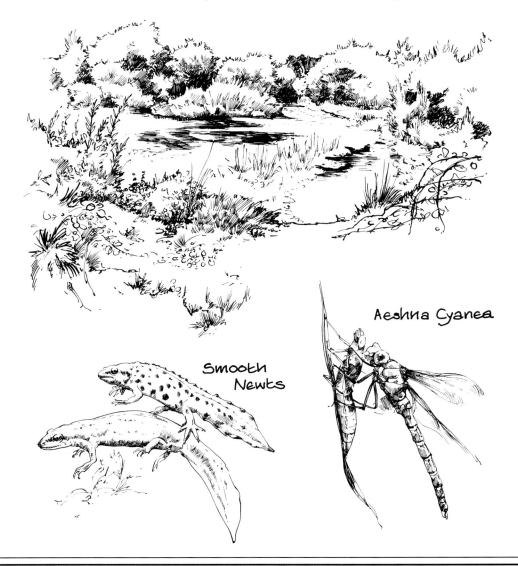

Aeshna Cyanea

Smooth Newts

of butterfly come to life in the warmth of the spring sunshine. Ivy-clad walls and trees are home to the first blue butterfly, the overwintering holly blue. The first white appears a little later when the green-veined white flutters among the hedgerows. One of the most attractive butterflies, the orange-tip, flies around mid-April and is seen along damp hedgerows or marshy areas where its caterpillars feed on the seed pods of garlic, hedge mustard and lady's smock. The males have the orange wing-tips while the females are similar to other whites except that the underside of the hind wings are quite patterned.

The red admiral is a migrant butterfly of the summer but some of the offspring do manage to survive the milder winters of the West Country and so may appear earlier than would be expected. The name admiral has nothing to do with the remarkable ability of this butterfly to find its way across the sea in the summer. It is a reduction of the original and more fitting name – red admirable. The peacock is another hibernator which emerges early in the season and cannot be confused with any other because of the prominent eye-spots on its wings which are designed to attract the death-dealing beaks of birds away from its vulnerable body. Up on the moors and heaths the Emperor moth, which has similar patterning, might be seen flying in daylight around the chosen foodplant for its young, which may be heather, sallow or bramble. The Emperor is one of the more spectacular of British moths and is the only representative in Britain of the family which includes the silk and atlas moths. It is the smaller male which flies during the day, the female being solely nocturnal. The moths are on the wing in April and the caterpillars can be seen in May. These amazing creatures are apple green in colour and are covered in a series of yellow warts with stiff little hairs sprouting from them.

Almost any stretch of water will have its quota of aquatic insects which are beginning to emerge from their watery nurseries in late spring. Aptly named, the mayflies make their appearance bobbing up and down over the streams, lakes and rivers throughout the region. Better known by most fishermen than by most naturalists, many of their names are well established as angling terms. These fragile creatures can be seen dancing over the surface of the water in swarms. The swarms are often composed of males only, rising and falling on delicate wings in an attempt to attract a mate. Courtship is brief and the female alights on the water to lay her eggs and set a circle of life in motion once more. From a biological point of view the mayflies are unique in many ways. Once adult, most insects will not shed their skins. Mayflies emerge first as 'duns' and fly to a perch where a further transformation takes place into the true adult. Sometimes this takes place in a single night and at most the adult will only live for a few days. Mayflies are truly ephemeral and live up to the name given to them by scientists – ephemeroptera. As always, nature is economical; these insects do not eat and so have no need of the complicated mouth parts found in other insects. They still have a digestive system, however, which acts as a float to keep them at the water surface while they lay their eggs.

Another insect which takes its name from the month of May is the May bug or cockchafer. These huge brown beetles can often be seen struggling on their backs beneath a lighted window from the end of April onwards. They are to be found in most wooded districts and along well-managed hedgerows where they form an important element of the diet of some of the larger bats.

On the warmer nights of spring bats emerge to feed on the increasing number of insects, themselves roused from a winter's sleep or newly emerged from pupae. The West Country is especially well provided for when it comes to bat species and it should not be difficult to see a number of different types on a dusk walk almost anywhere. Interest in bats has increased dramatically over the last few years, mainly and sadly as a result of their becoming rarer. The reasons behind the decrease in populations are complex and probably reflect a number of factors. There can, however, be little doubt that most if not all of these factors are a result of human activities of one sort or another. Disturbance in natural caves and mines during the winter are especially troublesome to bats. Insect-proofing chemicals in breeding roosts to cure woodworm and death watch infestations have taken a staggering toll, but loss of feeding habitat and the use of agrochemicals have also had an impact.

Cornwall and Devon have been perforated with mines for centuries and the activities of the last two hundred years or so have left a maze of underground tunnels which are ideal sites for daytime roosts and places for hibernation in winter. These artificial caves have allowed bats to spread into areas where they would otherwise be unable to live. Natural caves can be found in the limestone districts in Devon and many records are known from barns, church towers and even modern housing. The distribution of bats in the West Country is not precisely known, but anywhere where the combination of roosting and feeding sites are found is worth looking at. Many bats like to feed over water and the little Daubenton's bat has been recorded in a number of places, particularly canals where its habit of flying along their length just an inch above the water is quite characteristic.

Other bats will also visit water for the insects which emerge from it, and rivers and reservoirs are especially worth a visit if they are isolated stretches of water. Dozmary Pool on Bodmin Moor, the flooded china and ball clay pits of Bodmin and the Bovey Basin and the flooded quarries of Dartmoor are all good examples and well worth a bat-watching visit from late spring onwards.

Bats use echolocation for navigation and prey detection. The majority of the sound they use to bounce off objects is beyond human hearing and can only be 'picked up' by means of a bat detector. Some bats, however, emit at quite low frequency and sharp ears can hear the signals. The noctule, a hollow-tree rooster, often hunts in small groups over water and its chirps and clicks are usually quite audible. A much rarer bat is the large serotine, a bat found in old buildings and known to live in some church towers in East Devon and at least Restormel Castle in Cornwall.

BATS

Fourteen of the fifteen British bat species are known to occur within Devon and Cornwall, making the West Country a batwatcher's paradise. Of particular importance are caves, both natural and man-made, which provide the bats with roosting sites, while the variety of habitats which still remain cater for their different hunting requirements. Buildings, old and new, are also valuable sites for bats, and in common with the rest of Britain some bats, such as the pipistrelle and brown long-eared, are most often encountered in house roofs. Over the last few years our knowledge of bats has increased enormously and the public's appreciation of their plight has grown, but disturbance in hibernation sites and the use of insecticides for timber preservation mean that there is little room for complacency.

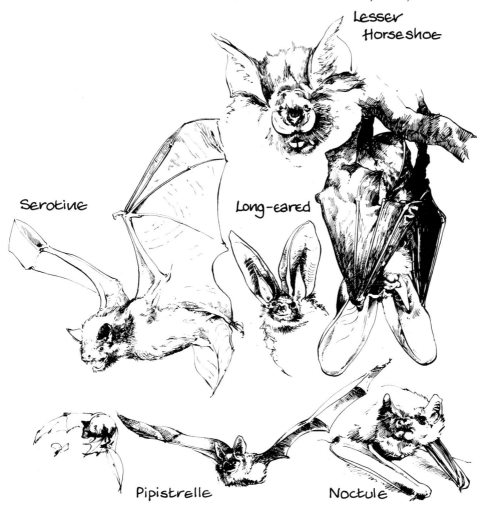

Lesser Horseshoe

Serotine

Long-eared

Pipistrelle

Noctule

Brown Hare

Pink Purslane

Painted Lady

Boxing Hares

Hoopoe

The real specialities for the West Country are the two horseshoe bats and the grey long-eared. The horeshoe bats are so called because of the peculiar leaf-like arrangement around their noses which are closely concerned with the high frequency signals they emit. On a bat detector these bats cannot be mistaken for any other species for their 'calls' sound like speeded-up canaries and are quite beautiful. These bats spend the winter in caves, and the summer in barns and other buildings. Devon and Cornwall have relatively large populations, but it must be remembered that the greater horseshoe is one of Britain's rarest bats. The grey long-eared bat is only known in the region from a handful of records although this may reflect the difficulty of distinguishing it from its close relative, the brown long-eared bat. Identification of bats in flight, even with a bat detector, is extremely difficult and handling bats is now an offence unless you are properly trained and licensed. This problem takes second place, however, when you are witnessing the aerobatic agility of these fascinating creatures. An evening spent watching bats in late spring, by the side of a peaceful stretch of water with the darkness gathering around you, is one of the most magical experiences in the West Country.

The spring period from March onwards is the time when another mammal is seen to best effect. Hares are thinly spread throughout the region and, it seems, have never been common. They appear to be less common in Cornwall than Devon, but they can be found around Cambourne, Penwith and Land's End. In Devon, a recent survey has shown their distribution to be patchy. The flat land of Exeter and Dunkeswell airports is a suitable habitat for hares and they are often seen on the fringes of Dartmoor in Devon and Bodmin in Cornwall.

The March hare, as anyone who has read *Alice in Wonderland* knows, is designated 'mad' and although its strange antics can be seen throughout the year this month is the best time to witness it. Hares, like many animals, are most active around dawn. By the time most of us are up and about the hares have gone to ground, quite literally, because they crouch in a shallow scrape called a form. In early spring the animals are more obvious in the fields and as the crops are still low they can be seen quite clearly as they leap, chase and box with each other, all part of the mating process. It used to be thought that the males were the 'mad' ones and the peculiar antics were part of defending territories or guarding a mate, but more recent research has shown that the females play a leading role and more often than not a pair of mad hares is made up of a female fending off the advances of an over-amorous male.

Although hares can live as long as twelve years, foxes and disease account for many of them before they attain such a grand old age. Changes in agriculture with chemical sprays and efficient machinery have also taken their toll and many a leveret gets reaped with the harvest. Interestingly enough the only reliable figures for the decline of the hare come from the shooting records of farms and estates and they reflect a significant drop over the last thirty years – there are, it seems, less hares to shoot than there used to be.

• *Permanent pasture near Land's End in April*

Hares require a variety of foods throughout the year and so unimproved farmlands of North Cornwall and Devon and some stretches along coastal cliffs are also good places to see them.

Down from the cliff-top grasslands which are also home to the hare, life is becoming more hectic in the rockpools. After the ravages of the winter storms the seaweeds are beginning their new growth and the button-like early stages of the thong weeds are forming. Although most of the creatures found are resident throughout the year some additional species come in to the pools to mate and lay their eggs. The liver-like sea hare will be seen in writhing masses before laying its eggs on a rock or sturdy alga. The eggs look, and feel, like strings of orange plastic. The sea slugs, whose beauty often contradicts their name, crawl up to the shallower water where they can sometimes be found in their hundreds. The common grey sea slug, a beautiful creature adorned with delicate outgrowths from its body, lays its tiny white eggs in a jelly-like mass which affords protection from predators, wave action and the heat of the sun. Many species of sea slug are quite small and only the careful observer will notice them but it is well worth searching for them for nature has painted them in bright exotic colours.

FIELD NOTES

SUMMER

Many people regard a stretch of golden sand backed by dunes as the ideal place to while away the days during a hot summer, the undulating dunes providing privacy and shelter for the sun worshipper. The very popularity of sand and sand dunes with the holidaymaker means that while these are perhaps the most diverse and interesting habitats for the naturalist they are the most visited and abused.

There are few large sand dune systems in the West Country which makes for even more person-pressure as visitors increase when the weather improves as summer takes over from spring. The north and west coasts of Devon and Cornwall exhibit the best examples and the system at Braunton Burrows is generally regarded as the most extensive system with an area of almost a thousand hectares. Such is the biological interest of this site that it has been designated as a National Nature Reserve and Site of Special Scientific Interest by English Nature and is recognised by UNESCO as an International Biosphere Site. It is now managed by full-time wardens to ensure that it survives. The difficult terrain and the similarity to parts of the coast of mainland Europe made it a natural practice ground for manoeuvres during the Second World War in preparation for the Normandy landings and the army still retains training rights so from time to time parts of the 'Burrows' are 'off limits' to the visiting public for their own safety.

At first sight sand dunes might seem unpromising places for wildlife with their vast tracts of marram grass and wind-blown sand. As with all habitats a closer look will reveal an amazing variety of plant life and the animals which depend on it for food and shelter. To gain a full appreciation of the complexity of the 'Burrows' the best place to start is as if you had just emerged from the sea and with your back to the surf of the Atlantic walk towards the dunes.

Sand is composed of grains of rock eroded by wave and blown by wind. A slight wind on the open beach soon results in a sandstorm of modest proportions and brings home the mobile nature of this substrate. The odd shell or piece of driftwood or seaweed acts as a natural barrier to the progress of the tumbling grains and soon a small hillock begins to form. More sand accumulates until a dune begins to form. Wind directions change, of course, and tides ebb and flow so many small dunes do not survive for more than a few hours at most. But some of them build up to large enough proportions to enable their survival. These are the dunes proper – massive mobile hills of sand which threaten to engulf anything in their path and which can attain a height of up to 30 m. From the strandline up to the sea-facing side of the sand dunes live a variety of plants, such as sea sandwort and prickly saltwort, species which can survive periodic inundation by a high tide.

Sand is an ideal material in which to study the succession of plants and although very few systems adhere to the theoretical 'straight line' development described in the textbooks a careful eye can pick out the evolution of a dune system from open sand to established scrub woodland. While in one area sand is constantly moving and smothering life, in the next plant life is colonizing the sand as a habitat.

Living on sand has two particular problems. First, the sand moves with every breath of wind, abrading or burying anything in its path, and secondly, it is

• *Wind-shaped dunes at Braunton Burrows*

very porous so that any water which falls upon it is rapidly drained away. Those plants which might be thought of as the first colonists of the new land must be well adapted to gaining a roothold and conserving their moisture so the plants of the fore dunes tend to be very hardy species. Few plants can survive on the seaward side of the dunes and the dominant species is the sea couch grass, which can only survive in the smaller dunes at the leading edge of the system and which rapidly gives way to marram, the most familiar plant of the sand dune community as you walk inland. Marram is a classic example of a plant which lives in the difficult conditions of the dunes; in fact it thrives where there is a constant supply of fresh sand and so over the years it can help bind the sand and build dunes of considerable height. The roots of marram can extend under the surface for some distance in their search for moisture. Where the spread is lateral and close to the surface new plants spring up along the roots to form the characteristic radiating pattern of growth which can be seen at the junction of vegetated and open sand, creeping ever forward as more sand is colonised from the parent plant. As fresh sand is blown in the shoots keep pace and can grow as much as a metre in a year.

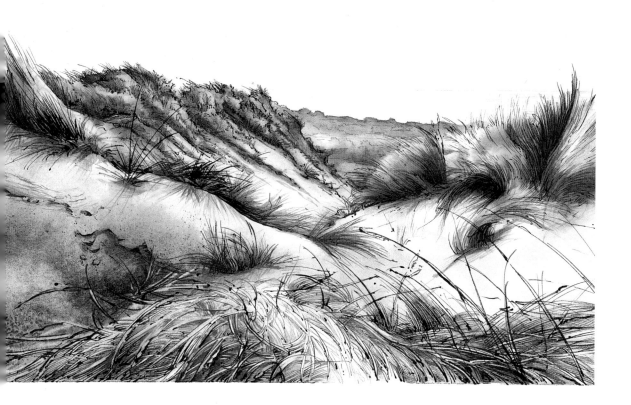

Open sand can be very hot and dry, so it is essential that moisture once gained is not easily lost. The sword-like leaves of the marram bear the secret of the plant's success. Like most plants, grasses transport nutrients through their tissues in solution and to keep them moving a certain amount of water has to be released by the plant. This is achieved at the leaf surface in most plants via tiny openings, or pores, called stomata. The speed of water transport is determined by the amount of water vapour at the leaf surface which is itself determined by weather conditions. So on a hot or breezy day the water vapour is quickly removed, the stomata are open wide and the water, as a vapour, flows freely. If too much water is released or transpired most plants will wilt as a means of closing their pores and many sand dune plants resort to this method for controlling the rate of water loss. Too much wilting results in the plant dying and this is a very definite threat on the bare sand of the dunes proper. Marram grass uses a variation on this theme but rather than the whole plant drooping it closes its leaves until the two edges meet to form a tube. Water vapour builds up in this tube and eventually reaches a point where the stomata are closed. When conditions are less threatening and marram has restored its moisture blance, more water can be released, the nutrients flow again and the leaves unfurl.

Such is the pioneering ability of marram that it is used as a major weapon in the fight against 'blow-outs' where the sand has become exposed by erosion and the wind is rapidly undercutting and blowing away the dune. Active conservation of dunes which have been eroded by military vehicles, scrambling motorcycles and the passage of many feet is a constant task on most of our dune systems and Braunton Burrows is no exception. Areas are fenced off from time to time and planted with marram in an effort to re-establish stability.

Marram seldom covers all of the available sand, and bare patches between clumps may harbour other species that are able to flourish in this harsh environment. Sea bindweed, with its delicate pink and white blooms, is a low-growing plant which creeps over the sand surface. Many species adapt to growing on sand by growing along rather than up. Leaves close to the sand surface prevent too much evaporation from the sand and keep essential moisture near the roots. A waxy surface to its leaves enables sea holly to hold its moisture and spines help to reduce water loss. Sea spurge stores its water in succulent leaves and has a large seed which contains enough moisture to ensure successful germination.

As is the case with most pioneering plants the better they are at their job the more competition they encourage from other species. As the tangle of roots and stem traps more sand and moisture and as the plants die and become mingled with the sand a more hospitable soil is created, a soil which is able to support less hardy plants than the marram which plays such a valuable part in 'fixing' the dunes. Mosses and lichens are among the most obvious plants of the next stage and where they occur in sufficient numbers to cover the ground the dunes take on a grey rather than white or yellow appearance and are known as grey dunes.

SAND DUNES

The often hot and dry conditions and easily drained soils of sand dunes make them one of the more inhospitable of habitats for plants. As always, however, nature is ready with pioneering species which, because they are specially adapted, can cope with the problems of existing in a near-drought and among ever shifting sands. The tall, coarse marram is a familiar sight on the foredunes, where drifting sands are necessary to stimulate its prodigious growth rate. The deep root system binds the sand and seeks for water while the drinking straw-like leaves can curl in on themselves to hold water vapour and slow down water loss.

Retaining moisture is most important for plants on sand and succulent plants are common among sand-growers. Saltwort and stonecrop are almost cactus-like, with swollen leaves for storing much-needed water. Preventing water loss in a usually breezy and hot habitat is a problem overcome by many species by having waxy leaf surfaces, a strategy adopted by the spurges, along with a long tap root for obtaining water. These tenacious plants help to establish the dunes by trapping sand, holding moisture and adding their dead tissues to the inert grains to provide a reasonable soil and a foothold for less hardy species which will come after them.

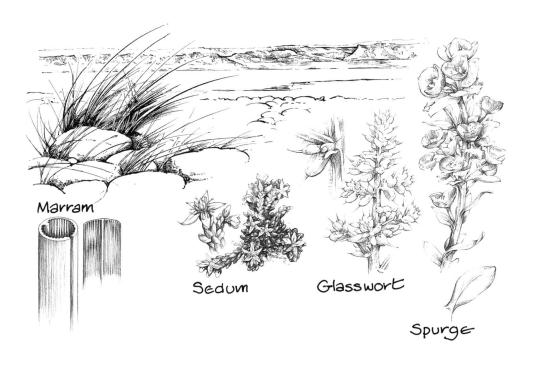

Marram

Sedum

Glasswort

Spurge

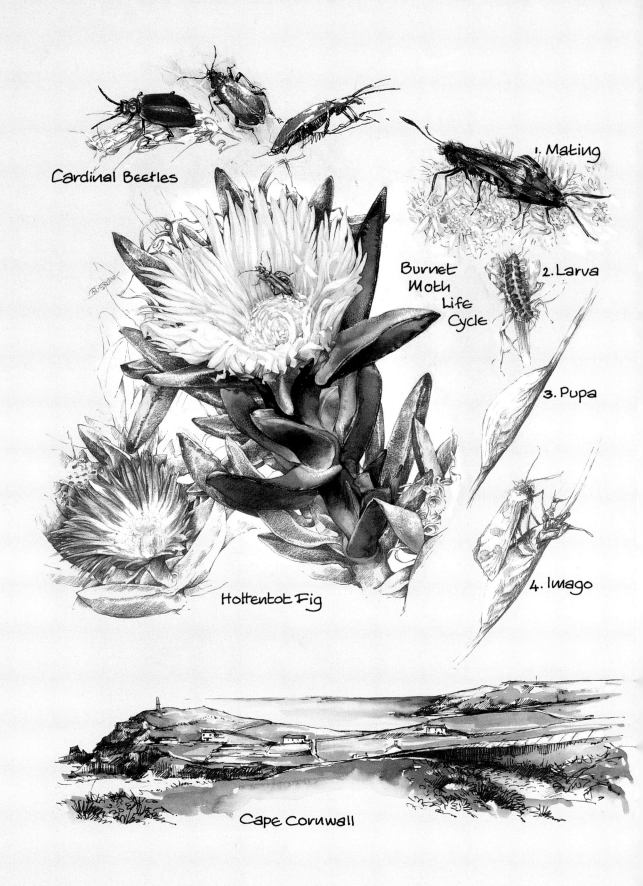

Cardinal Beetles

1. Mating

2. Larva

3. Pupa

4. Imago

Burnet
Moth
Life
Cycle

Hottentot Fig

Cape Cornwall

They hold enough moisture at ground level to encourage other species to grow. Still relatively poor in nutrients, this soil is the home of clovers, vetches and trefoils which like other members of the pea family can take nitrogen directly from the atmosphere with the help of symbiotic bacteria held in nodules on their roots. Every farmer knows the value of a fallow crop of clover for returning 'goodness' into the soil and the otherwise poor sand is enriched as these plants die and decay.

Despite more permanent vegetation, water loss can still occur and many plants have a hairy covering to their leaves as an aid to conserving moisture. Among these are plants such as great mullein, comfrey and the beautiful red-flowered hounds-tongue, which gains its name from the rough texture of its barb-covered seeds. Here also are the tall, brightly coloured, but delicately petalled evening primrose, the tiny periwinkles and the delightful sea pansy. The composite family is well represented with golden rod, fleabane, ragwort, spearwort and the tough carline thistle whose golden petal-like bracts will last well into the winter.

Out of the wind, protected by the dunes and at little risk from inundation by sand, are the flat-lying dune slacks. During the winter months these may be flooded for weeks at a time and even in all but the driest summers some of them remain damp, with the water table rarely far beneath. In an attempt to increase the already outstanding interest of the 'Burrows' ponds have been dug and there is now the likelihood of standing water in places for most of the year. Such a patchwork of habitats close together can support an amazing collection of plants, some of which clothe the ground in large numbers during their flowering season. Where the ground is damp the striking yellow of the marsh marigold provides a blaze of colour as if to herald the spectacular orchids which spread in a carpet as the summer moves on. Pinkish-purple marsh orchids and the crimson and white marsh helleborines proliferate, but there are other species to look for, such as the yellow-green petalled fen orchid and common twayblade. The sedges and rushes like to keep their roots wet, and grow well in the areas of damp slack. About twenty species can be found from the familiar bulrush to the rare round-headed club-rush. Grasses, too, such as common reed and floating sweet-grass are to be found especially in the wet slacks. The beautiful quaking grass is a common plant of the damp slacks. The yellow rattle, named for the sound its seeds make as they rattle in their pods, the restharrow, tallish and pink flowered, and the amazing strawberry clover with flower heads which look just like the fruits after which it is named, can be seen among the creeping willow and grasses. There are three rows of slacks at the 'Burrows' and each has its own character depending on exposure to the salt-laden winds from the sea, the amount of erosion it suffers and the chance arrival of seeds and spores.

Moving away from the sea and out of the slacks the soils are more hospitable and sand-loving plants give way to those of the dune pasture. Among the

• Coastline at Cape Cornwall

grasses, species which are familiar on inland pastures are common. Annual and smooth mallow grasses mix with cock's foot, sheep's fescue and yorkshire fog, providing the backdrop for many species of flowering plant. The tall rosebay willow herb is one of the more obvious plants and there are the species of the composite family including beaked hawksbeard, common knapweed, lesser burdock, creeping thistle and even the rare sneezewort. The tall spikes of the viper's bugloss are easy to spot while the tiny, exquisite eyebrights and wild

54   • *Marbled white and small copper butterflies near Pendeen Watch*

thyme require you to kneel at ground level if you are to appreciate fully their perfection.

Although the 'Burrows' is best known for its flowering plants, with a total of over 400 species, it is also a mecca for the entomologist. The myriad blooms attract a huge variety of insects. Butterflies rise in clouds as you walk through the knee-high grasses, and the common blue, dark green fritillary, marbled white and gatekeeper should all be easy to spot. The jewel-like small copper is

especially pleasing as it glints in the sunlight. Closely related are the brilliant scarlet and black burnet moths whose papery cocoons can be found on almost every grass stem in some places. The poisonous ragwort is the food plant for the striped orange and black caterpillars of the cinnabar moth; they are immune to the toxins and even absorb them into their own bodies for protection. The bright colours act as a warning for birds that the caterpillars, and later the moths of the cinnabar and the burnets are distasteful, and so they can feed and fly in broad daylight confident that they will be left alone. Once a bird has learned its lesson the hard way by eating a caterpillar it will leave them well alone in future. The time to see moths at their best is at night, and being by the coast the 'Burrows' are especially liable to provide temporary homes for some of the more spectacular migrant moths such as the large hawkmoths.

At each step the ground springs into action with hundreds of grasshoppers whose chirping accompanies each summer's day. With a little practice the different songs can be recognized as the males of mottled, meadow and field grasshopper each serenade their females and keep other males at bay. As dusk falls these songs are replaced by those of the nocturnal bush-crickets. Difficult to find because they are such wonderful ventriloquists, the two more vocal species are the dark bush-cricket and the magnificent great green bush-cricket. Some individuals appear to have a formidable sting at the rear end. These are the females, and the 'sting' is actually the egg-laying device and quite unable to deliver a wound. A word of caution is necessary, however, as the great green bush-cricket can give quite a powerful bite if mishandled.

The wetter areas are home to dragonflies. The presence of water at the 'Burrows' also means that frogs are found, as is the palmate newt, with its webbed hind feet and filament-like tip to the tail in the male. Hot, dry areas usually suit reptiles and the common lizard is often seen as a scurrying blur as it scampers for cover. Not only is the high calcium content of the sand good for some of the more unusual plants but it also means that molluscs can find the materials to build up their shells. Piles of empty snail shells are often to be seen among the dunes where they have been carried by birds intent on the succulent morsel within. The banded snail is quite large and easy to spot despite the bewildering number of patterns it assumes as camouflage to hide it from birds. The real speciality of the 'Burrows', however, is the beautiful, but rare and protected sand bowl snail.

The diversity of invertebrates on the dunes attracts larger predators. Where the soils are more stable and richer the burrowing common shrew forages for worms, but the open dunes are the home of the pygmy shrew, a surface-living mammal which feverishly hunts out beetles, spiders and harvestmen. Early morning is the best time to see what has been happening the night before as the normal elusive mammals leave their tracks as evidence of their nocturnal wanderings. Foxes and hedgehogs travel quite considerable distances and are easy to track over the sands. Woodmice and the two voles – bank and field –

Generally thought a woodland plant, gladdon grows on Penhale Dunes •

SHREWS

Pygmy, common and water shrews are to be found throughout the West Country wherever the habitat suits them. As its name implies, the largest species, the water shrew, is often found close to clean streams and ponds, where it dives and swims in search of its prey. Hair fringes on its feet and a keeled tail adapt it to life in the water, but this is not a totally aquatic species and it usually returns to land to eat its victims and to clean and dry its fur before its next foray. The common shrew, despite its name, is not ubiquitous and is absent from those areas with sand or waterlogged soil which prevent it from burrowing and from finding earthworms – a favourite food. The pygmy is perhaps the most widespread shrew, being quite capable of finding almost anywhere the small spiders and insects upon which it feeds. The slatey-coloured upper side of the water shrew makes it unmistakable, but the other two species are more difficult to separate; both are brownish in hue and can be similar in size. Tail length, provided it has not been artificially shortened by a predator, can be a guide: that of the pygmy is generally more than two-thirds of the body length, while that of the common is usually about a half of the body length.

Water Shrew

Common Shrew

Pygmy Shrew

Shrew Skull

Pygmy Shrew

Common Shrew

Water Shrew

provide food for visiting owls and kestrels and the evidence of the rabbit's presence is to be seen everywhere.

The combination of dunes, pastures, scrub, adjacent marshy areas, the open sea and the Taw Torridge Estuary make Braunton Burrows an area of exceptional interest to the birdwatcher. Skylarks sing their hearts out high in the sky and the thickets are always worth looking at (or listening to) for whitethroats and even lesser whitethroats may be seen and heard.

While Braunton Burrows is undeniably the most important sand dune system in the south-west of the region there are others of smaller size in various parts of Devon and Cornwall. Elsewhere in Devon Dawlish Warren is of note, claiming the title of the warmest nature reserve in Britain. At the mouth of the Exe Estuary the Warren is a unique double sand spit formed by the constant battle for supremacy of the sea's currents and the flow of water from the River Exe. Formerly the Warren was more extensive than now and the channel between its tip and the town of Exmouth considerably smaller. A certain amount of stability is gained from the groynes which prevent wind-blown sand from being carried away completely and the Warren is protected by a number of preventative measures against erosion of all sorts. As with other dune systems in Devon and Cornwall the same principles of formation and colonisation apply as those described for Braunton Burrows. Many of the plants are the same species living in the same conditions. If Dawlish Warren owes its uniqueness to the presence of the warren crocus, a tiny plant found growing among the fine turf of the links, it owes its mass appeal to its birdlife. Though it has something to offer the birdwatcher throughout the year, its main interest is during winter and spring when migrants are coming and going daily. In Cornwall, where sand dunes are known as towans, they occur mainly on the north coast. Hayle, Constantine and Sennan are especially well known to both the holidaymaker and the naturalist.

At first sight the moorland areas appear uniform and uninteresting, vast tracts of browned vegetation split here and there by a small river valley, solitary trees and, of course, the characteristic tors. Dartmoor, the largest area of moorland in the West Country, has been described as the last great wilderness but the hand of man can be seen to have been at work. Cattle and sheep graze at liberty and ponies seem to pose for photographs at every opportunity. Dry-stone walls disect the landscape in some places and old mine workings are still resisting nature's efforts to reclaim them.

It has been suggested that Dartmoor was once one of the most densely populated parts of the West Country; for the archaeologist it is a treasure chest of hut circles and standing stones, stone rows and cairns. Prehistoric man would certainly have seen a very different Dartmoor scene, maybe one largely covered in trees, later to be cleared for agriculture or tin streaming. Grazing is now the major controlling factor on all of the moorland areas and it is the teeth of the ponies, cattle and sheep which keep the moors looking the way they do. To many people moorland brings to mind rolling country with vast areas of purple heather, and indeed heather is among the dominant plants of some parts of the moors in Devon and Cornwall. Grass moors predominate in some parts of Dartmoor and the encroaching bracken gains more ground each year, protected from destructive periodic fires by its deep roots which are ready to spring up with uncurling green fronds each spring.

Exmoor aside, granite is the base of all the moorland in the region and it is this hard rock which ensures that the moors stand above the surrounding countryside. Altitude brings with it rainfall; the moorland vegetation is

• *Stone row on Hangingstone Hill, Dartmoor*

reflective of the high annual rainfall and more importantly the large number of rain days in a year. Dartmoor is a wet place, although on a hot, dry day in midsummer this seems hard to believe. In a hot spell the lowly mosses become shrivelled, crisp and brown, looking for all the world as if they are dead. Towards the end of summer when there is more rainfall they absorb water in quantity and are given a new lease of life, becoming green once more. Their capacity for holding water is enormous, some of them capable of containing many times their own weight, sphagnums being perhaps the best example. It is to these mosses that we owe our water supply; where they cover large areas

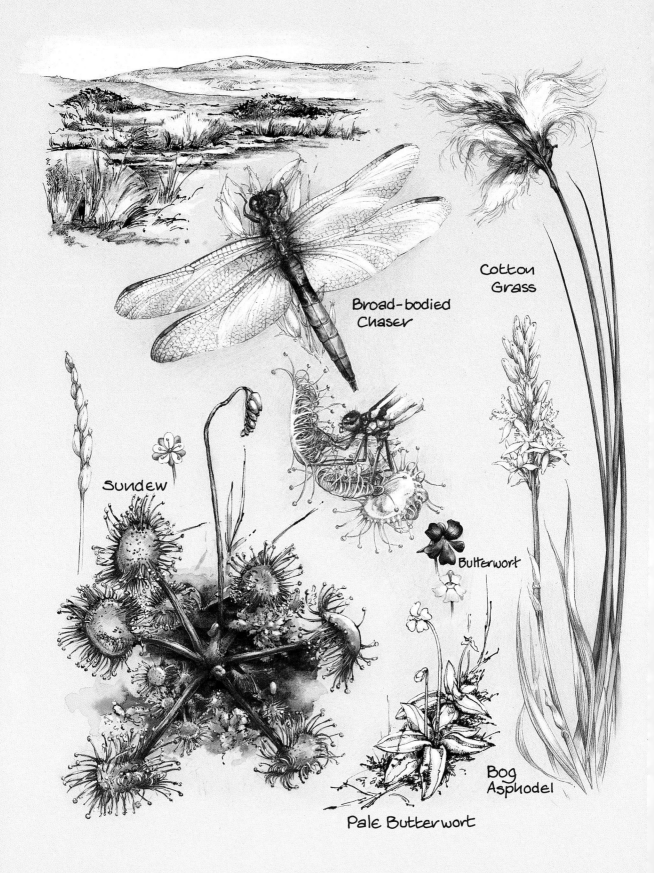

Broad-bodied
Chaser

Cotton
Grass

Sundew

Butterwort

Bog
Asphodel

Pale Butterwort

they act as huge sponges, and Dartmoor, for example, can be thought of as an enormous natural reservoir from which most of the rivers of the region draw their water.

Over thousands of years, dying mosses gradually build up to form thick deposits of peat, useful as a fuel in the past and now wastefully spread on gardens to improve the texture of the soil. The soft cushion-like texture of mosses once proved ideal for the stuffing of pillows, much as it cushions tired feet on a trek across the moors. While they are useful and abused by humans, mosses play an important role in nature. Despite their diminutive size they colonise bare ground, claiming new territory and making way for other plants to follow. Mosses can survive on some fairly poor soils and when they die they add their vegetable matter to the mixture, enriching it and allowing less hardy plants to gain a foothold. A species of moss called the 'Charcoal Burner' is one of the first to colonise recently burnt ground where it protects the soil, gives it moisture and helps it back to health.

Some of the mosses can be extremely beautiful. The bright-green feather mosses and the silvery-coloured thread mosses clothe trees and river banks. The golden star-like 'flowers' of the 'Goldilocks', a moss found on the moors, are really rosettes of leaves – mosses are not flowering plants but reproduce by means of spores held in cups at the end of slender threads. The spores are carried away by the wind and some of the cups explode when a drop of rain hits them, others opening gradually to reveal the tiny grains which will start the next generation. At first glance a carpet of moss appears to be quite uniform and dull but it is actually a mosaic of colour and texture which contains a whole world of other plants and tiny creatures alive and kicking while the rest of nature is quiet and hiding in the heat of the day.

Vast blanket bogs form on the upland areas, while valley bogs are noticeable from a distance as bright green slashes in the steep river valleys. Almost every flush has its boggy community and it is extremely difficult to walk a valley side without getting your feet wet. The moorland bogs are notorious as traps for livestock as well as aimlessly wandering humans; certainly as the mists descend without warning, even in summer, it is very easy to become lost and to end by sinking up to your knees in a cold muddy bog. Where a thick layer of mosses have accumulated and a crust is formed on the top the quaking bogs may be found. Looking remarkably solid it is only when you venture out on to the surface that you realize you might have made a mistake. The whole surface begins to ripple with every footfall for you are really walking on a floating mass of vegetation, and while the water below might look clear and open the sponge is completely saturated. The greenness of the boggy areas is a good guide as to where to be careful. Among the sponge-like sphagnums, however, are a whole range of plants perfectly adapted to living under such conditions.

The nodding heads of the cotton grasses give the first indication of damp conditions. A largish clump might from a distance appear to be a very white

• *Boggy moorland species at Fox Tor Mire, Dartmoor*

sheep and a more extensive covering gives the impression that unseasonal snow has fallen. The mire behind Fox Tor on Bodmin is one of the more concentrated areas but cotton grass is to be found wherever there is a boggy margin. Bare areas on the edges of the bogs or on the raised peat hags are worth investigating for some of Britain's most fascinating plants, the sundews and the butterworts. Permanently saturated ground and a low mean temperature make life difficult for plants to extract the necessary minerals from what is already an acid and inhospitable soil and so some plants resort to a carnivorous habit in an attempt to supplement their needs. The butterworts have a rosette of sticky leaves which attract insects on to them and make them stick on the surface. Rather than a rapid snap the leaves gradually curl over and incarcerate the victim. The sticky fluid is similar to our stomachs fluids and digests the soft parts of the fly, the resulting broth being absorbed by the plant.

A much more attractive insect-eater is the sundew. The leaves of this plant are covered with small red tentacles and a large number of these plants gives a blood-like impression. Each tentacle bears a dew-like globule of glue and the whole leaf surface has the quality of an open hand bearing jewels to tempt a passing insect. Just one misplaced leg on a drop of glue and all the tentacles close in for the kill, bending over to prevent the insect's escape and sealing its doom, holding and digesting at the same time. The round-leaved sundew is the more common of the two species likely to be found and is easily distinguished by its leaf shape from the intermediate sundew which has longer strap-shaped leaves. Insect-eating plants obtain nitrogen from their prey, a nutrient which is missing in poor waters of the bogs in which they live.

A very attractive plant to look for is the erect, multi, yellow-flowered, bog asphodel. Its Latin name has a sinister ring to it and recalls the folklore with which it is associated. *Narthecium ossifragum* is the hollow-stemmed plant which was believed to cause broken bones and indeed it was once thought that any sheep eating the plant would suffer from a thinning and fracturing of its skeleton. Bog voilet, ivy-leaved campanula with its blue flowers and the pink bog pimpernel grow among the purple moor grass and the bog bean can be found in areas where open water exists. The water itself can be very highly populated with plants, although many of them are microscopic. The tiny desmids, single-celled algae, are among some of the most attractive of aquatic species but you need a microscope to appreciate them fully. It has been estimated that there are in excess of 1000 species on the moors, so if you are interested in plants you will find the area a source of endless fascination.

Despite the almost continual presence of water, many of the moorland plants live in a state of drought; the cold acid water is difficult to take up and so these plants have a variety of methods of keeping their water. Gorse has leaves which are reduced to spines, many of the grasses have thin needle-like leaves and the ling has tiny leaves covered in water-retaining hairs, which give it its characteristic downy appearance.

Clapper bridge at Tor Wallabrook, Dartmoor •

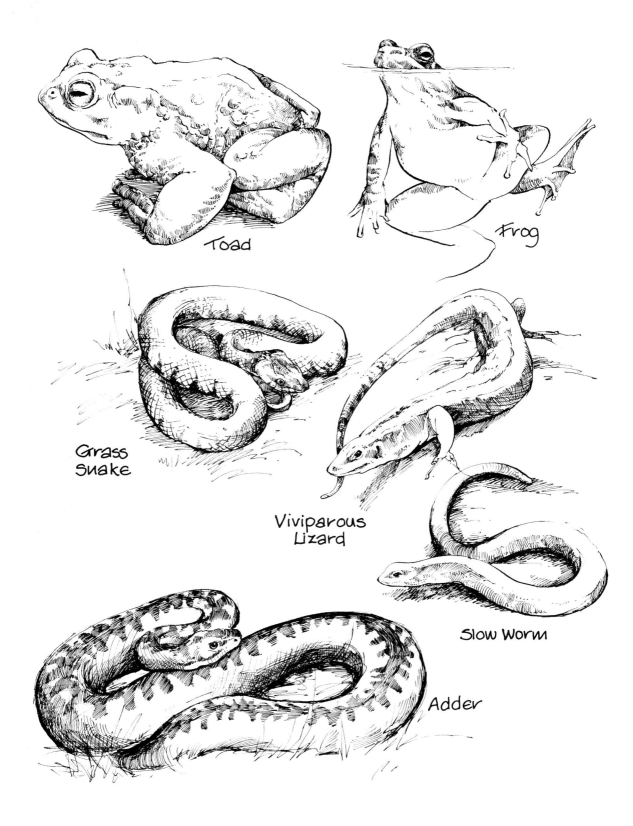

Toad

Frog

Grass
Snake

Viviparous
Lizard

Slow Worm

Adder

Wet moorland is attractive to a variety of animals if only because it is a place to get a drink. The extensive blanket bogs are perhaps less productive than the valley bogs if only because their size precludes entry of many animals. Molluscs are to be expected wherever damp conditions prevail but the lack of calcium severely restricts the number of species to be found, although the large black slug is almost ubiquitous in these areas.

Strong fliers are represented by the dragonflies which flit as nature's jewels above any patch of water. Especially dramatic is the golden ringed dragonfly, which can be seen wherever there is a fast-flowing shallow stream for the females to lay their eggs. The many streams which filter from the bogs and join up to form the rivers of the region are home to a variety of aquatic insects. Crawling on the bottom are the neat caddis flies complete with their protective cases, composed of twigs or small stones. Above the water the mayflies dance and where tall grasses or reeds emerge from the water the spent cases of the previous generation of damselflies and dragonflies can be found. Brown trout shoot out from bank to bank disturbed by a passing shadow and are themselves food for the largest regular visitor to the higher moors – the shy and elusive otter. Wet peaty mud on the banks might reveal the footprints of this magnificent mammal and large boulders are worth investigation for tell-tale droppings or spraints.

Another water-loving mammal is the mink. Introduced from North America, this animal is now to be found on many of the rivers of the West Country. Like the otter, the mink leaves droppings as territorial markers and as a means of communication with others of its kind. Mink scats are less pleasant to the nose than the spraints of the otter, the odour of which has been likened to the smell of new-mown hay.

Mammals on the high moor are not common, especially on the wetter parts, but the tiny pygmy shrew is one of the few mammals which can be found here. Unlike its very similar relative, the common shrew, it does not burrow and it does not rely on earthworms as its food. As a surface-dwelling animal it feeds on spiders, harvestmen and other surface invertebrates. During the summer months these can be plentiful and a stroll across the moor is always accompanied by the chirping of grasshoppers, easy food for the insectivorous shrew. The common shrew may occur in some of the drier areas where there is a good depth of soil and even the mole can be found at high altitudes if the conditions are right.

Rabbits are perhaps the most numerous mammals on many parts of the moors and have an undoubted controlling influence on the vegetation. Although rabbits have a long association with moorlands they were in fact originally introduced by man soon after the Norman Conquest. A domesticated species, they were kept in warrens and looked after by warreners. On Dartmoor in particular many place names have been derived from a nearby warren – Warren House Inn, Trowelsworthy Warren and Huntingdon

• *Reptiles and amphibians found in the West Country*

Warren are examples. Rabbits no doubt escaped from warrens over a long period of time and started to breed in the wild, but from the fifteenth and sixteenth centuries onwards many of them filtered into the wild, establishing themselves as efficient denizens of the moors. Rabbits do have an effect on the vegetation and their close cropping is very apparent around the new wild warrens. Ponies and sheep are also important in keeping the moorland vegetation in trim and it has been argued that these three animals are responsible for maintaining the character of the moors as we see them today.

Where cover allows wood mice and other rodents to flourish the adder is to be found, and perhaps avoided. This is Britain's only venomous snake, but it is not the major threat to the moor walker that many people believe. Most adder bites are the result of carelessness when the snake is deliberately provoked or accidentally disturbed. The majority of snake bites are on hands, as ramblers climb stone walls or on the feet and ankles when the snake is trodden upon. Watching where you put your hands and feet and wearing the right footwear should be sufficient protection. Adders are really quite elusive and sightings do not reflect their true numbers, for many of them slither quietly away on the first approach of a heavy-footed human.

Wet patches and pools are the home of frogs which can be seen in large numbers in the early summer. Larger pools and flooded quarries are the places to look for newts. The most common species is the web-footed palmate newt but the smooth newt is also to be seen. Courtship takes place in the early summer when the male, curled into a 'U' shape with tail aquiver, approaches the female. After mating each egg is carefully concealed in a leaf of pond weed. One of the more accessible flooded quarries is Hay Tor Quarry. Hay Tor itself is one of Dartmoor's 'honey pots', well known and easily reachable places where large numbers of visitors are encouraged to congregate. It can be recognised from some distance by the broad well-trodden path which has resulted from the tramp of countless 'adventurous' feet, but it is still worth walking up and around the back to find the quarry. This shallow broad pond is an oasis for a variety of animals and rewards a visit, especially in the early morning or late afternoon. It is here that for the first time I witnessed cuckoos mating along the fence, a convenient perch really intended to keep livestock and people from falling down the side of the quarry. Flooded quarries, small clumps of trees and bushes and the clitter slopes are the best places to search for the birds of the moorland for otherwise they are spread fairly thinly – a reflection of the scarcity of food.

The birds of the open moorland are limited, but three are almost ubiquitous. The carrion crow manages to find a living by scavenging among the tussocks of grass and heather and the smaller jackdaws may be seen amongst the tors, but neither should be confused with the majestic raven. A loud cronking sound above your head is usually the first indication that there are ravens about and a glance at the sky should reveal the presence of Britain's largest crow flying

Farmland near Ravens Tor, Dartmoor •

overhead. The raven is a bird which is surrounded by myth and superstition, fitting for a bird of the misty moors. It has been hounded throughout history and must now be regarded as uncommon; there are an estimated 100 pairs in Cornwall and it is 'numerous and widespread' in Devon. Certainly it has fled to the more remote parts of the West Country to nest on the high, inaccessible sea cliffs, and the tors of the moors, but it is difficult to go for a moorland walk without seeing, or at least hearing one as it flies between roost and feeding

69

grounds. The call and flight of this bird have been described as ponderous and it is these characteristics which immediately identify it from the other black crows – the carrion crow and the rook – when in flight. It is a massive bird and a good-sized raven will reach 62 cm in length, with a heavy bill. It really is an attractive bird and a closer view will show that it is not entirely black but suffused with iridescent purples, blues and greens. Unfortunately anyone close enough to see these metallic sheens in the past was probably close enough to kill the bird, and it has long been regarded as a pest amongst lambs and other young livestock. The raven will eat just about anything which is edible, including a lot of carrion. During the lambing season the raven can be a useful bird, devouring the ewe's placentas and any dead or dying lambs. Any carcass will attract most of the ravens in an area whence they will rapidly strip it, so preventing blow flies and other sheep pests from breeding, a practice which has earned them the title of vultures of the sheep country. Ravens are often portrayed as wise old birds in cartoons and fairy tales. Both of these characteristics are true to a point for ravens are regarded, along with other crows, as being among the more intelligent of birds and they can live for more than fifty years. Traditional nesting sites are used year after year, and the granite tors provide ideal inaccessible places.

More often associated with the fringes of moorland, where trees are available for nests and where farmland may provide food is the buzzard, the largest raptorial bird likely to be seen in the West Country. In days gone by the buzzard was often referred to as an 'eagle' or a 'kite' and so care should always be exercised when reading older accounts of the birds of the district. Sadly, the real owners of these names are no longer to be seen in the region. I can think of no better token of summer than the mewing cry of the buzzard as it circles with wings outstretched and feathers spread looking as if it is holding long-fingered hands open to catch the sun's rays. The buzzard is common in the West Country and you can almost guarantee to see one wherever you travel. The open expanses of the moors are especially rewarding for the cry is far reaching and the birds fly so high that they can be seen as dots in the sky from way off.

Like all birds of prey the buzzard has had its share of persecution in the past, and even in the relatively remote areas of the West Country its numbers have fluctuated with fashion and fate. The sixteenth-century Preservation of Grain Acts allowed the destruction of almost anything that could be thought as vermin and put a price on its head. Birds with hooked beaks and sharp claws were obvious candidates and so the buzzard suffered. Later when game preservation and management was in its heyday the buzzard was again regarded as an enemy, but it was the indirect action of myxomatosis in 1954 which caused a dramatic drop in numbers and few pairs bred in the following year. This was due not to the disease itself but to the lack of rabbits – a major food item of the buzzard at that time. Fortunately the buzzard was adaptable and turned to smaller mammals such as voles and mice to help it over the crisis.

Buzzards may often be seen on the ground where they are hunting for a variety of much smaller prey which includes earthworms, caterpillars, beetles and lizards as well as carrion. On the ground or in the air the buzzard is a magnificent bird but when aloft, soaring on the warm air of summer it is a triumph of nature. Soaring flight is very efficient, the birds gaining height with the least amount of effort. Hot air rises against the faces of the tors to provide the uplifting thermals on which the buzzards appear to float. Gliding at height has obvious advantages in that the bird is able to cover more ground in search of prey and their staggering eyesight enables buzzards to spot quite small animals on the ground. Buzzards nest on the moors and solitary trees are worth a second look. I almost passed by one such tree but my attention was drawn to something glowing white among the branches. It was a virtually complete vertebral column of a sheep which had been interwoven with the more normal nesting materials of twigs, macabre perhaps but quite striking.

The other common raptor of the moors is the kestrel, which is quite at home building its nests on the ledges of tors and abandoned quarries. Two other small birds of prey are worth noting, the merlin and the hobby. The hobby is essentially an insect feeder and should be looked for where dragonflies and grasshoppers abound. The merlin is much more at home among the short vegetation where its prey of skylarks and meadow pipits find nesting sites. This, rather than larger birds, was the hawk favoured for 'ladies' practising falconry. Once released, it flew directly up to attack its prey and dropped straight back to the ground close by.

The skylark is easily located if not easily spotted for, like the buzzard, it is usually seen as a speck against the summer sky. With wings beating wildly, pouring forth its far-reaching song, the skylark is the epitome of summer gladness as it proclaims its territorial challenges to other males and its 'come-ons' to females, from its aerial 'songpost'. On the ground the bird scuttles between the moorland hummocks to and from its nest so as to confuse any predator nearby and in its rare periods of rest its characteristic crest allows it to be easily recognised. Similar in appearance is the meadow pipit, a bird which it is hard to believe manages to survive at all. As if being the favourite food of the merlin were not enough the meadow pipit is also the chosen host of the cuckoo on the moors.

Sound plays a very important part when it comes to finding birds on the vast expanses of moorland and the sound of two stones being knocked together means that stonechats are about. These attractive birds are often seen perched on boulders with tail aflicking as they object to your presence or make contact with a mate. Approach too close and the birds fly away, the brightly coloured male with his black head and russet breast, as usual making a more attractive spectacle than the subtly coloured, brown-streaked female. Another chat-like call might be that of the wheatear, which gets its name from the white patch on its rump rather than from any preference for ears of wheat in its diet. It is of course an insect-eater. The white rump is absolutely distinctive and enables the bird to be identified readily in flight as well as at rest; the male is grey on the back and buff underneath.

In the wet flushes a snipe may be disturbed from its nest but it is only one of the waders which forsake the lowlands of winter for the highland breeding grounds of summer. The warbling cry of the curlew seems out of place, but this bird and the rarer golden plover are both moorland nesters.

In more northerly areas red and black grouse are birds of the moors, but neither species can be regarded as common in the West Country. Many other species of birds will stray into or fly across the moors but in general the moorlands of the West Country are not regarded as the most rewarding sites for birdwatching.

The lack of large numbers of birds on the moors, both wet and dry, is probably due to a sparsity of insect prey necessary to support them, but there are some insects which are characteristically found on the moorland areas. Among the lepidoptera one of the most striking is the emperor moth. As its name implies this is a large species and the males are often to be seen flitting among the heathers during daylight. The females are more normally night-fliers but both have obvious eye-spots which serve as some protection from the depredations of birds. The caterpillars are handsome, too, being a brilliant apple green with orange profusions from which black bristles erupt. Despite their bright coloration they can be difficult to locate as they are superbly camouflaged among the growing heather upon which they feed. They are the only representative of the family of moths which contains the silk moths and like their commercially reared cousins they produce a silken cocoon for the protection of their larvae during the transformation through the chrysalis stage to the adult.

By far the most commonly found moth of the moors is the fox moth. Again its caterpillar is large and obvious, but is protected from most predators by being clothed in irritating hairs. Most birds prefer to avoid getting a throat full of itching caterpillar and so leave them alone, but the wily cuckoo has the ability to eat these, usually unpalatable, insects. As would be expected, the grass-feeding butterfly caterpillars predominate among the moorland vegetation and so the meadow brown, gatekeeper and small heath may all be seen. One of the most attractive butterflies, the green hairstreak may be sought wherever bilberry flourishes. Bilberry moorland is especially productive, but many hedgerows also contain this plant and are well worth a careful look. The hedges around Dozmary Pool, for example, almost always reveal this delightful gem of an insect.

The large, toy-like, dor beetles are dung feeders and so can find plenty of food on the moors wherever livestock is found. They themselves are food for foxes and occasional badgers, which deliberately turn over the cow pats and pony droppings in search of their prey.

The short vegetation of moorland, especially where there is regeneration after peat digging or burning, is home to the mottled grasshopper. This species blends in perfectly with the dark soils found between new shoots and is one of the first colonisers of this type of habitat. Other grasshoppers likely to be seen are the meadow grasshopper and on the drier areas the field grasshopper. All grasshoppers are, of course, more likely to be heard rather than seen, except when they leap among the vegetation. The meadow grasshopper has a chirp which sounds rather grating and continuous, while the field grasshopper is a series of short 'ssit' sounds. Often two males will take part in a duet where one sings in the intervals between 'ssits' of the other. The mottled grasshopper chirps a quiet buzzing sound.

To the casual observer heathland and moorland are very similar; but although they have many plants and animals in common there is one quite distinct difference. Moorland, even dry moor, usually has a high soil moisture content yet the plants which grow upon it show many adaptations towards retaining water. This is because the moors are at high altitude where the overall temperatures are low and water uptake very slow. On heathlands, which are generally low lying, similar adaptations occur but this is due to lack of water over most areas. In effect both plant communities are living in drought-like conditions. On the moors it is physiological (there is water but it is difficult to take up), while on the heaths it is a physical drought (there is simply a lack of water). Confusion can arise because there are dry and wet heaths just as there are dry and wet moorlands and the problem is further exacerbated by some heaths being called 'moors'. Sometimes both moorland and heathland are locally called commons, areas where commoners have certain rights. Ventongimps Moor, a Cornwall Trust for Nature Conservation Reserve, and Mutter's Moor in East Devon are both heathlands.

The total area of heathland in Britain has been drastically reduced over the last few hundred years as a result of development of one sort or another and so the few remaining areas are of immense importance. As far as the West Country is concerned the most important areas of heathland are those of The Lizard and Land's End Peninsulas in Cornwall and the area known collectively as the East Devon Commons. These have not escaped change; while the general area might have stayed the same, over the centuries they have become fragmented and do not sustain the variety of plants and animals they used to do. Despite this they do support some wildlife and are some of the most attractive and varied areas within the region. Heathlands are particularly susceptible to mismanagement, and over-grazing, over-enthusiastic burning (swaling) and failure to control encroaching vegetation have all taken their toll on this disappearing habitat. Many of the heaths actually arose as the result of human management but have been around for so long that they are part of the 'natural scene'. It is only when they are absorbed or abandoned that their true value becomes apparent.

During the summer the East Devon Heaths are a blaze of colour, the two dominant plants being bright yellow gorse and purple heather. Dwarf shrubs such as these are most characteristic but on the fringes stands of Scots pine provide dramatic landscape features and birch adds to the variety. The East Devon Heaths are sometimes known as Pebble Bed Commons from the underlying bedrock which is responsible for the well-drained soils, but where a clay layer comes to the surface wet flushes occur and carry a similar vegetation to the smaller bogs of the moors.

A particular speciality of the heathlands is Britain's most beautiful warbler, the Dartford warbler. This bird has had a mixed history and is very susceptible to harsh winters. One of the few birds which relies on an insect diet throughout the year, it has a southern distribution. Heathland is its ideal habitat and the species feeds among the gorse but nests in heathers. Indeed it almost has the gorse to itself with only the occasional whitethroat showing any sign of competition. In common with moorland the two species of birds which are most often seen are the skylark and the meadow pipit.

Unlike moorland most heathlands have at least some parcels of taller shrubs and trees as part of their mosaic and this scrubby vegetation is attractive to a greater diversity of birds. Among them is the nightjar, a summer migrant more often heard than seen as its eerie churring echoes across the open heath. The nightjar is a ground nester and as such has an almost perfect camouflage; if resting on the ground it blends with leaf litter and if on a tree it matches the bark, becoming part of a dead branch. Nightjars are nocturnal birds and the ideal time to see and hear them at their best is just after dusk. First one bird will churr and soon all of the others within the area will join in, each proclaiming its territory. Nightjars are quite curious birds and will come to check up on any intruders. If you are fortunate you may witness the wing clapping which is part of the display flight. Otherwise nightjars hunt on silent wings, scooping insects into their wide feather-fringed mouths as they fly. An injured bird flopping along the ground is not what it might at first appear to be. The likelihood is that you have strayed too close to a nest hidden in the heather and the bird is tempting you away. The first instinct is to leave the bird alone but it may be better to follow the parent as it slowly lures you away from its young. I was especially lucky one night when I witnessed a training session with a whole brood of fledged nightjars dropping onto a path in front of me, each dragging a 'broken wing'. The churring sound of the nightjar has been likened to the sound of a spinning wheel and the bird has been given the nick-name of wheel bird because of this.

In the course of listening for nightjars you may hear what sounds like an angler reeling in his line. Only the fact that you are miles from open water and it is dark tell you that you are mistaken. Your next guess might be some kind of insect like the cicadas heard abroad, and again you would be wrong. Despite the fact that no grasshopper, in Britain, makes a sound like the one you are hearing the bird which does produce this peculiar song is called the grasshopper warbler. Like the nightjar the sound is continuous but seems to waver up and down; the bird produces it by turning its head from side to side as it calls. Also, as is the case with the nightjar, such an obvious call might attract the wrong company and so both birds have the amazing ability to throw their voices. They can thus be quite difficult to pinpoint.

These East Devon Heaths provide a stronghold for the delicate and attractive, though rare, silver-studded blue butterfly. This species lives in isolated colonies and any further destruction of heathland can only lead to its decline, for it seems that it is not a butterfly which migrates to 'pastures new' when threatened. The life-history of the large blue butterfly, which includes 'adoption' by an ant colony during its caterpillar stage, is well known, and the silver-studded blue forms a similar association. Larvae are often taken into the nests where they provide 'honey dew' in return for their keep and the obvious protection of the ants.

In common with the moors the heaths are often very wet, and small boggy areas form, exhibiting many of the plants already mentioned for the moorland bogs. In some cases these heathlands have been 'enhanced' by creating or improving other habitats within them. On the Royal Society for the Protection of Birds Reserve at Aylesbeare and Harpford Commons streams are kept clear; this encourages dragonflies and damselflies, including the rare species, the southern damselfly (*Coenagrion mercuriale*).

A series of ponds have been dug which are true oases for wildlife in the sometimes unbearable heat of the exposed heathland. The larger dragonflies constantly patrol their patch here, and the clashing of wings as rivals meet may often be the only sound you hear on a drowsy summer's afternoon. Hundreds of pairs of damselflies flying in tandem haunt the surface as they search for an egg-laying site. Alighting on the surface of a leaf of water weed the female manoeuvres herself and her passenger so that she can dip her abdomen beneath the surface to plant her egg in the tissues of the leaf. She is sometimes almost submerged and would be very vulnerable if it were not for the clasping male upright and ever vigilant for a competing male or a predator. At the slightest threat he lifts himself and his mate clear of the water and into the air.

In the boggy areas the real speciality insect is the brightly coloured bog bush-cricket. Although it may look like a grasshopper and long ovipositor (not a sting) of the female and the long, fine antennae at once distinguish it. This bright insect clambers among the rank vegetation tempting you to follow it as it leaps and crawls clumsily from plant to plant. It seems to know that the further into the mire it takes you the sooner it will be safe and it is not long before you give up the chase after sinking thigh deep into the morass which it calls home. Bush-crickets are often mistaken for true crickets after their habit of chirping at night, but the trilling notes of the wood cricket are only now to be heard in a few places in the West Country. The scrub woodland fringes of the heaths are, fortunately, among these places. The high-pitched continuous song is best heard in the late afternoon and early evening when the insects leave their leafy lairs among the litter to sing.

Out of the heat of the day, at dawn and dusk, the ponds attract a host of thirsty animals. Deer tracks are common in the dried mud and a glimpse of these animals as they come down to 'the water hole' for a drink is a regular occurrence. Water is, of course, absolutely essential for amphibians and the ponds attract toads and frogs for spawning. Wherever there are frogs and a relatively undisturbed habitat grass snakes can be expected and a quiet approach to the waterside may reveal one of these beautiful creatures actually swimming in pursuit of its slippery-skinned prey. The grass snake is the largest species of snake in Britain and can attain a length of more than 1.2 m. As such it should be easy to distinguish from the only other species you are likely to encounter in the region – the adder. Being non-venomous the grass snake is a perfectly harmless species. The olive-green/brown colour is ideal camouflage among the waterside vegetation, but the distinctive yellow and black collar should clinch the identification for you.

Other reptiles are more at home in the drier parts of the heaths, and the common lizard is often to be seen basking on the open areas where cover is close at hand. Most often lizards are overlooked and the only sign of the presence at all is a blur and moving vegetation as they dive for cover. All of the reptiles are very sensitive to vibration and as such should be approched with extreme care. You are most likely to observe one by sitting quietly in a likely place. Occasional records of the extremely rare and magnificent sand lizard have never been verified and it should be assumed that this creature is no longer to be found anywhere in Devon and Cornwall. The adder on the other hand, with its zig-zag markings and venomous bite is to be expected on all the heathlands of the West Country. Like all reptiles it is shy and would prefer to avoid contact with humans where possible. Its characteristic pattern, although obvious out in the open, serves to camouflage it when hidden among vegetation and it can be difficult to see in the scrub next to paths across the heaths. It is, however, a snake which is remarkably faithful to particular sites and may well be regularly encountered in the same place at the same time of day. This makes life easy for the observer who has disturbed a specimen for it may well be 'waiting' for you the next time you quietly approach. Part of the growing process of all reptiles is the shedding of old skin and an especially bright example might be showing off a new glossy coat. Conversely, a dull-looking snake with milky-looking eyes is just about to cast its redundant outer covering. Old skins do not last long out in the open, but a freshly shed skin, often in one piece if it is from a snake, provides an almost fingerprint-like representation of the animal even down to the contact lens-like eye covers.

The southerly tips of Britain around Land's End and The Lizard have an especially interesting group of heathlands. The Lizard, in particular, is formed

of some of the oldest rocks in the area and the various minerals which they contain have a dramatic effect on the soil content, making it acid. This, in turn, dictates the type of vegetation that grows here. The spectacular coastal scenery of this area is complemented by a unique series of heathlands, providing one of the most fascinating areas in the British Isles – a fact recognised in 1976 when it was declared a National Nature Reserve. Thirteen hundred hectares of this almost Mediterranean locality is now protected. It is for the botanist that The Lizard is particularly interesting; many of its plants are regarded as national rarities and walkers are requested to keep to the footpaths to avoid trampling over and destroying them.

The typical, and predominant, colours of heathland are to be found on The Lizard, but here the yellow is provided by the dwarf western gorse and the delicate lilac by the rare Cornish heath. Other characteristic plants are the black bog-rush and the usual purple moor grass. Where conditions remain wetter for much of the year the dwarf and pygmy rushes, both rarities, are to be seen. As expected of poorer soils the clovers do very well and seventeen of the twenty or so British species are to be found, including further rarities such as the twin-flowered clover; this species, as its name implies, has paired flower heads of pale pink and superficially resembles the commoner knotted clover. The influence of the sea is never far away and sand quillwort, hairy greenwood and the wind-resisting, low-growing sea asparagus give the botanist something to note.

While The Lizard Peninsula is arguably the botanical highlight of the West Country, there are many other examples of coastal habitats, not least of which are the numerous cliffs. The two counties of Devon and Cornwall share between them something like 500 miles of coastline and much of this is composed of cliffs. Access to this valuable series of habitats is now possible as a result of the establishment of the Coastal Footpath system, although its popularity might itself be a threat to the wildlife it harbours. A walk along the coastal footpath is a journey back through millions of years for the coastline is made up of a variety of rock types of different ages, from some of the oldest in the region dating back 350–400 million years (The Lizard) to some of the most recent. All these rocks are affected differently by weathering and so produce an ever-changing vista to the walker as well as a variety of niches for wildlife. Different soils support different plants and animals and the ever-present influence of salt-laden winds ensures that the narrow strip of land along the tops of the cliffs, as well as on their faces, leads to a unique series of habitats.

Dense jungle-like vegetation flourishes along the East Devon coast from Axemouth to Lyme Regis in Dorset where the slipped cliffs provide an almost endless variety of niches for a bewildering number of species of plants, insects and the birds which feed on them. Here the cry of the peregrine can be heard as it leaves its precipitous cliff nesting site to go in pursuit of an unwary pigeon.

Sea cliffs are home to a fascinating flora, especially where the bedrock is composed of limestone. The headlands near Torquay are carpeted with the

Typical summer flora of The Lizard •

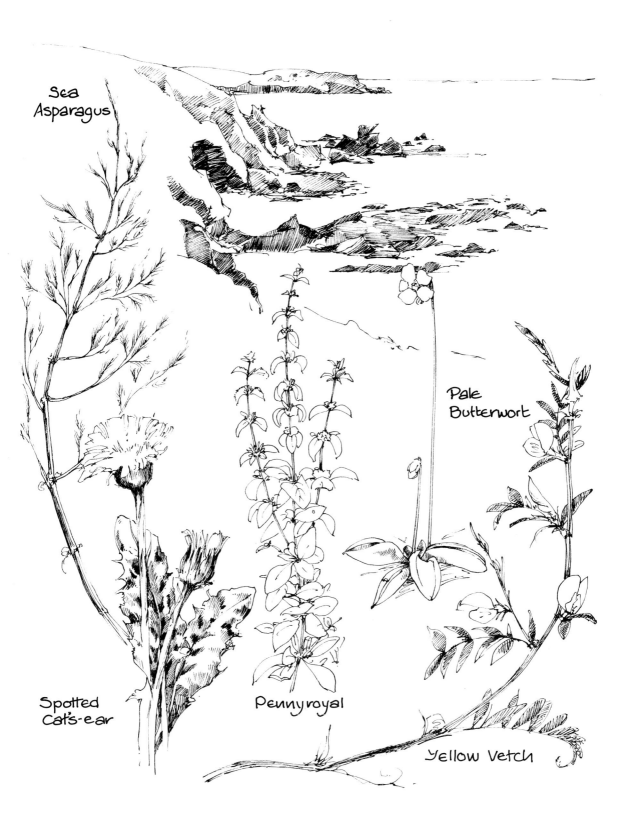

Sea
Asparagus

Spotted
Cat's-ear

Pennyroyal

Pale
Butterwort

Yellow Vetch

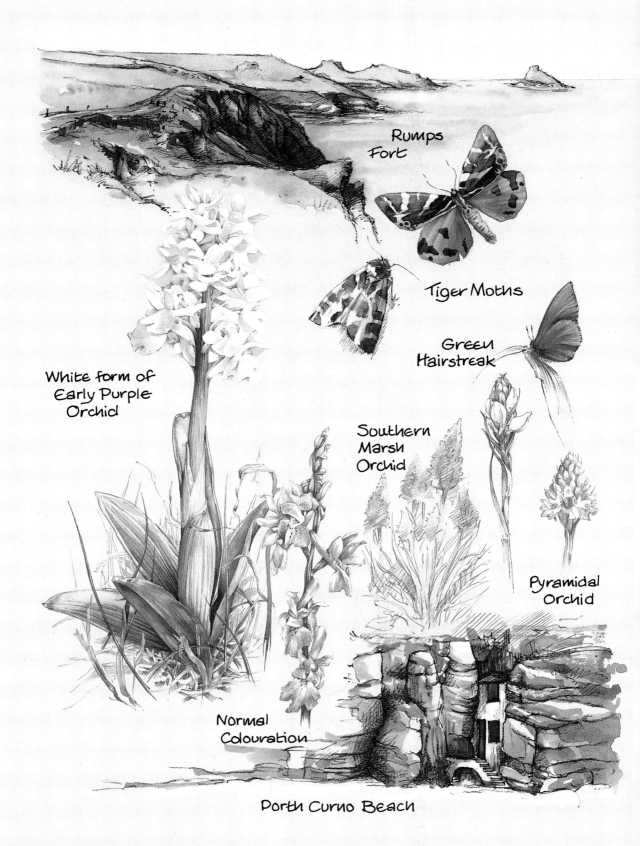

Rumps Fort

Tiger Moths

Green Hairstreak

White form of Early Purple Orchid

Southern Marsh Orchid

Pyramidal Orchid

Normal Colouration

Porth Curno Beach

sweet-smelling wild thyme and the tiny-flowered, exquisite eye brights. The tough-leaved, pink-flowered thrift adds much of the colour to the exposed cliffs and water-retaining plants like samphire and stonecrops thrive along the coast. The lime-loving wild clematis or traveller's joy scrambles over lesser shrubs, gaining the life-giving rays of the sun with the support of its neighbours. The dominant shrub along much of this stretch of coast is blackthorn and the ever-present bramble erupts from the short, rabbit-cropped turf, the mammals giving back something in the form of droppings. Sea beet, nettle, white campion and many other plants gain help from the nitrogen-rich bird droppings, while the vetches and trefoils add a burst of colour to the more impoverished soils.

Chalk, a particular type of limestone, has its own characteristic flora, the cliffs near Beer representing a good example. At the top of the cliffs chalk downland predominates, with short turf and a dense mix of other plants. The yellow-flowered creeping cinquefoil, the clover-like black medick and the bird's foot trefoil cling to the ground among yarrow and mouse-ear hawkweed. Common rock rose, purging flax, both field and small scabious and later on in the summer the beautiful Autumn gentian are to be found among many others. A closer look at any blue butterflies is worth the effort for the rare chalk hill blue has recently been recorded in this area and the long-tailed blue has been seen close by near Branscome.

Branscombe is also home to one of the more restricted of our bush-crickets. The grey bush-cricket lives among the pebbles by the sides of the cliff path as it descends to the beach. All along the south coast during the summer a watch may be kept for migrant butterflies. Clouds of red admirals, clouded yellows and painted ladies can be seen coming in from the sea. The day-flying Jersey tiger moth is a speciality and sometimes occurs in numbers so large as to cover all of the vegetation for metres in either direction. North Devon and various parts of Cornwall such as The Lizard and St Agnes are occasionally graced with a visit from the large and stunning monarch butterfly. This species is North American and undertakes incredible migration flights within that continent. Fairly frequently some arrive along the West Country shores as a result of natural 'drift' or as unwitting stowaways on board ships.

The early summer sees the sea birds nesting on some of the more inaccessible cliffs wherever ledges are formed. Among the crows the county bird of Cornwall, the chough is, sadly, no longer seen in its former haunts in Cornwall, the last finally giving up the struggle in 1973. However, a pair did appear back on the cliffs quite recently and there is always the hope that they might return again. Jackdaws, on the other hand, find cliffs throughout the region to their liking and nest in considerable numbers. Likewise the 'street pigeon' is very much at home along the coast, an interesting phenomenon because the wild form of this most familiar bird, the rock dove, which is a cliff-nester, is now regarded as a rarity. The stiff-winged fulmar is a common sight

SHAGS AND CORMORANTS

The name 'parson' usually coupled with a locality is given to both cormorant and shag where they occur around the coasts of the Devon and Cornwall peninsula. The shag is more of a seabird than the cormorant, which can now be seen many miles inland on reservoirs and rivers where it may compete with humans for fish, but both are familiar sights around the rocky coasts throughout the year. The shag is the smaller, more elegant bird of the two, with iridescent green plumage and a crest, while the cormorant is more sombre and sports a 'clerical collar'; younger birds have a pale front. On the water these birds have the ability to 'sink' until only their necks are above the surface, from which they dive in pursuit of fish, using their powerful webbed feet for propulsion. The slender neck looks as though it could only swallow small fish but one cormorant was seen to eat a 1 kg salmon and another was caught with a 75 cm conger protruding from its throat. Despite being aquatic birds, shags and cormorants both suffer from waterlogged wings if they stay in the water for long periods and they have to return to land where they spread their wings to dry out the feathers. Their characteristic habit of flying low over the water gives them extra lift and makes flight less strenuous.

along much of the cliffs, particularly in North Devon and Cornwall, but it is also seen along the south-coast cliffs around Torquay and in East Devon.

A seabird census carried out in 1969 and 1970 showed that there were about 400 pairs of cormorants breeding within the two counties, the majority being in South Devon and Cornwall on isolated stacks and offshore rocks. The smaller, crested shag is much more of a mainland cliff-nester and its numbers were about twice that of the cormorant. The north coasts of both counties are especially favoured and colonies at Baggy Point and between Combe Martin and Lynton, in North Devon and Godrevy Point and Gurnard's Head in Cornwall are among the largest. Both birds are known as 'parsons' from their dark colour and upright posture and they often borrow the name of the locality, Ladram Bay Parson for example. They are to be seen flying low over the water gaining extra lift and thus cutting down on the amount of energy they expend. These two species dive from the water surface in pursuit of the fish which are their prey and can often be seen standing on a rock with their wings stretched out to dry before they make their next sortie beneath the sea.

A pair of binoculars will prove helpful when watching gannets fishing offshore. Flying in flocks of up to 200, these dramatic birds can be seen at all times of year wherever the fish upon which they feed are to be found. Constantly searching the surface for the tell-tale flash of light reflected from fish they fold their wings and drop like darts onto their prey below. The harsh cries of the terns are a constant accompaniment along the coast and though smaller than the gannet this bird is equally impressive as it drops in on its sand eel prey. Britain's most common breeding gull is the herring gull and there is barely a stretch of cliff that does not provide a nest site for this species. The most delicate of the gulls, the kittiwake, is much more restricted, however, and is found on the cliffs near Torquay in Devon and around Land's End and The Lizard in Cornwall. The largest colony in the West Country is the one on Lundy off the north coast of Devon, which is also the home of the comical-looking puffin. Other gulls to look out for are the greater and lesser black-backs, and among the auks guillemot and razorbill can be seen in many of the localities already mentioned. Interestingly enough the common and black-headed gulls which join us in the winter months do not breed anywhere in this area of the British Isles although in the case of the latter many non-breeders remain throughout the summer.

Cliffs can provide a good vanatage point for watching seals, especially in North Cornwall, and if you are very lucky a chance sighting of the elusive otter, (a regular coastal visitor), an occasional whale or more likely acrobatic dolphins. Only one species of mammal is especially associated with cliffs and that is the feral goat. These animals live a wild existence along the Valley of the Rocks near Lynton in North Devon where they occasionally challenge the coast walker for posession of the footpaths. The badger, an animal more usually associated with woodlands has adapted well to living along cliffs and the colonies near Branscombe in East Devon are said to be among the most concentrated anywhere in Britain.

Another creature you may sight from the cliffs during the summer is Britain's largest fish – the basking shark. This huge, but harmless creature is often seen off the coast as it cruises at the surface, dorsal fin showing in true shark-like fashion with its snout raised and mouth open to gather the tiny plankton upon which it feeds. There does seem to be a predictable pattern to where these monster fish are most likely to turn up. Lines of floating seaweed often indicate where water is being pushed up from the seabed carrying algae and nutrients with it. Such areas are ideal for plankton to feed in and basking sharks have been observed to take advantage of these concentrations when feeding. Small fish are also attracted to this source of food and they in turn attract fish-eating gannets and gulls which may indicate the possible presence of basking sharks.

Periodically the sea coasts of Devon and Cornwall receive visits from huge shoals of giant jellyfish. These large, beautiful, pulsating creatures cause scares among bathers fearing that they are being attacked by Portuguese men o' war. These colonial 'jellyfish' which occasionally drift in with the Gulf Stream are easily recognized by the larger gas filled float which acts like a sail. A smaller wind-blown jellyfish is the 'By-the-wind-Sailor'. Giant jellyfish are easily spotted from the cliff tops as shoals of them are carried in on the tides, but it is when they are washed up on the beach that their real nature is revealed. The translucent 'bell' or 'umbrella' is the organ of propulsion; below it can be seen short, stubby tentacles which act as filtering mechanisms for this jellyfish captures its prey by sieving tiny animals from the plankton and not by powerful stinging cells. It is thus harmless. Other jellyfish of the summer are the common jellyfish with its four mauve circles, and the delightful compass jellyfish. The ballet-like swimming of jellyfish is best appreciated when they are in open water and so if you are landbound cliffs, quays and headlands provide an 'aerial view'. Jellyfish are food for a number of larger animals and it is at this time of year when some of the whales may be spotted in search of this prey. Recently an increasing number of turtles have followed the jellyfish from warmer climes and may become stranded on the beaches, especially along the north coasts. The Gulf Stream brings with it other exotic organisms. Scouring the beaches of North Devon and Cornwall may reveal some of the tropical seeds which have drifted in with the tides.

For most of us the sea remains a mystery but mother nature treats us to some idea of its extent each time the tide ebbs and flows. Sandy beaches are uncovered and with them some of the life which exists below the surface. On some beaches the sand mason worm can be found in its thousands, the surprisingly tough sand-covered tubes left on the surface giving an idea of the life which remains hidden. The delicate tests of the sea-potato (a kind of sea urchin) are commonly found on beaches around Torquay and Dawlish.

The most obvious debris left on the shores, however, are the seashells. The sand–living molluscs are more delicate in structure than their counterparts of the rocky shores. Here can be found the long razor shells and the fragile, subtle-tinted tellins. Carpet shell and cockle are common, as are the huge otter shells. Washed in from just offshore are the turret shells and the exotic-looking pelican's foot. Where currents work to gather shells in a particular place by a sea wall or groyne, for example, many species can be found in a small area. Barricane Beach in North Devon is rightly called Shell Beach, for here must be one of the greatest concentrations of species to be found anywhere within the area. The whole beach is made up of shell fragments among which can be found entire individuals of many species. Violet sea-snail, the amazing elephant's tusk-shell and the daintily sculpted wentletrap are just some of the more prized species, a tiny sample of the life which exists beyond the surf.

Cornwall, and especially Devon, are agricultural counties and wherever you travel the influence of farming is to be seen. There are, however, some interesting areas of farmland which have escaped, for one reason or another, the intensive chemicalisation which most agricultural land has suffered since the Second World War. Of special interest and only recently the subject of concern are the unique Culm Grasslands. These unimproved and often damp grasslands are home to a vast number of animals and plants and are the nearest we have to the wild-flower meadows, which provide memories of youth for our parents and grandparents. The character of Culm Grassland varies with the amount of water around and the area is perhaps best thought of as a jigsaw of heath, fen and grassland which has been managed by man. As such the grasslands are semi-natural as opposed to completely wild, but they are none the less important to the naturalist. Centuries of summer grazing have ensured that scrub has been kept at bay and the herbaceous plants have flourished in the 'unimproved grassland'. Odd fields hidden away in corners, and stretches of 'rough' ground are prime areas for bringing into more 'efficient' agriculture, forestry and recreational use. As such Culm Grassland has gradually been eroded until something like 50 per cent has been lost in recent years; it is only the efforts of the conservation bodies which will ensure its survival. The Devon Wildlife Trust is actively acquiring Culm Grassland Reserves in an effort to prevent any further loss, and one such reserve is at Rackenford Moor, in North Devon.

Among the plants of this unique habitat are many which are uncommon and some which are rarities, such as the whorled carraway and wavy St John's wort. Orchids and scabious give a splash of colour, while meadow sweet adds to the perfume which fills the air. Insects are found here in profusion, including the rare marsh fritillary. Good cover for small mammals also means good hunting for the barn owl, again an increasingly rare species. Once a familiar sight along roadside verges and old meadows the barn owl has declined drastically in recent years until it is now regarded as a threatened species. The presence of barn owls and the absence of chemicals is more than mere coincidence, and in other areas

loss of habitat and consequent lack of food is held to be a major cause of its demise. As its name implies it is a bird which lives in farm buildings; while once it benefited from rural construction industries it is now suffering as the old barns are converted into expensive homes. This beautiful owl is the banshee of legend, ghostly white on silent wings as it deals death to an unsuspecting mouse, vole or shrew. The Culm Grasslands are important for other birds, too, and during the early part of the summer provide nesting sites for some of the waders, such as lapwing and curlew.

Perhaps the most obvious feature of farming has been the construction of the many miles of hedge, wall and ditch which demarcate human territories and act as stockproofing and windbreaks. The banked hedges so characteristic of the West Country might differ in the way they are constructed from area to area but they all are of tremendous wildlife value. Hedgerows when properly managed are wonderful refuges for a host of animals and plants. Like most habitats the longer they have been established the more interesting they are likely to be. Hedges can be thought of as linear woodlands, where there are shrub and herb layers below trees left as standards. In the past these would have been cropped for timber. In general terms hedges gain more species of shrub as the centuries pass and it can be interesting to apply the 'Hooper Method' to hedge dating; you walk along a 30 m stretch of hedgerow and count the different shrub species you find, and for every shrub you add one hundred years to the age. So a hedge with three shrub species is about three hundred years old, for example. This is obviously a very rough and ready method and is only really accurate when taken into consideration with other methods, such as old documentary evidence. None the less it is a good way of really looking closely at hedges and discovering the amazing life they contain.

Elms were a dominant hedgerow tree until the advent of Dutch Elm disease killed most of them off. Ash, hazel, beech, holly, and oak are all common hedgerows trees in the West Country. Many species of shrub provide the main body of the hedges. Elder, hawthorn, blackthorn, hazel, dog rose and bramble are most commonly found. A well-managed hedge fulfils all of the purposes it sets out to do: it is stock (and people) proof, it marks the edge of different holdings or fields, and it acts as a windbreak. Devon and Cornwall are rightly famous for the luxuriant growth of plants which lays hidden among the deep, winding country lanes. High humidity means a strong growth of ferns, particularly in the North Devon lanes; the banks which support many a hedge in this area are ideal habitats for the unfern-like hart's tongue and the male and lady ferns. The rich dark-green umbilicus-like leaves of the navel wort, also called penny wort, are a common sight. Later in the summer the erect flower spikes add a touch of cream to the overall verdant appearance. The white flowers of the greater stitchwort mingle with the pinks of cranesbills, red campion and herb Robert and the tall foxgloves provide a welcome nectar source for the many bees which are found here. Blue flowers are represented by

• Barn owls need the shelter of old farm buildings

forget-me-nots and the green alkanet. Violets grow among the stems of the taller plants which also provide support for climbers like cleavers, honeysuckle, greater bindweed, ivy and wild clematis or traveller's joy. Where verges exist orchids are a common sight and some unusual species such as the tall greater butterfly and bee orchids can be found. Closer to the sea alexanders are

Navelwort

Roche Rocks

increasing and in some places line the roadsides almost to the exclusion of other plants. The plant itself is very attractive but the smell is foul, except to insects to whom the rotten aroma proves irresistible. The flora of the hedgerows depends upon soil and aspect, management and humidity and is inevitably variable.

Dense hedgerows can support many species of insect and when in full flower prove a magnet to the winged hordes. A few moments of close hedge-watching reveals a whole world of action; some insects are in search of nectar, some are looking for a place to lay their eggs and others to feed on the other visitors, themselves providing food for larger insects. A hot summer's day sees the hedgerows alive with colour and movement as butterflies flit from bloom to bloom, or defend territories from a favourite perch, spiralling in mock battles before they return to rest. Most hedges have some nettles where the small tortoiseshell, peacock and red admiral will be found. Brambles are attractive to the gatekeeper, and the hedge and garlic mustards provide egg-laying sites for the superb orange tip. The holly blue is found wherever there is holly and ivy and the delicate green hairstreak takes advantage of the bird's foot trefoil along the verges. Buckthorn attracts brimstones, and the whites are ubiquitous where there are crucifers. Hoverflies of many species are regular visitors to the umbellifers, which are also attractive to the pollen-gathering flower beetles, including the brilliant metallic green oedamera. Red soldier beetles, which are carnivores, take advantage of the visiting hordes. Despite their rather frightening appearance the scorpion flies are quite harmless and although they are also meat eaters they rarely attack live insects, preferring to feed on those which are already dead.

A walk along the hedgerows on a sultry night may reveal a brilliant glow worm with its pale-green light. The green glow is usually brightest among the females, curious grub-like creatures which are attempting to attract a passing male. Pretty though the light is these insects are carnivorous and feed on small snails which they narcotise before they eat them. In this way the snails are kept fresh over a day or two as the glow worm gorges.

The wealth of insects provides a steady supply of food for shrews which can be heard scurrying among the tangled vegetation and occasionally screaming at each other as they meet at a territorial boundary. The large insect populations of the linear woodlands are food for the bats which regularly visit them at night; the tiny pipistrelle and the large noctule are the two species most likely to be encountered as they patrol the lanes in search of prey. Woodmice and bank voles are the two small rodents most likely to be seen in the hedge bottoms, while the rare dormouse is more likely to be found as it clambers about in the branches above ground. If there are brambles and hazel in a hedge then it is worth looking for dormice as these are their favourite foods; stripped honeysuckle stems are an indication that this pretty, russet-coloured mammal has been nest building. The nest, about the size of a cricket ball, may be discovered by a careful observer but once found should, of course, be left well alone. Where hedges meet in the corner of a field and there is some rank growth the even more elusive harvest mouse is a likely sight. The idyllic life in the hedgerow for these small mammals is always at the risk of predators and the two most feared must be the weasel and the stoat. If you spot either of these animals be patient, for they are insatiably curious and will return further along the hedge to spy on you; thus a second, and more prepared, period of observation is almost always guaranteed. Both animals are long and thin, and brownish in colour with cream or white underparts. The stoat is generally the larger and always has a black tip to its tail. Both are still persecuted by some gamekeepers, which is most unfortunate for they are rarely guilty of a crime against game and in fact are beneficial in that they keep many mammal 'pests' in control. It is impossible to say just how common these mammals are for sightings tend to be fleeting and they are extremely difficult to study in the wild. Much more obvious are the diggings of rabbits and foxes, both of which find hedges ideal bases for their foraging expeditions into adjoining fields. Similarly, the badger sometimes makes its home along the edges of fields in the security of the man-made barriers.

As woodland has been eroded hedgerows have become a more important habitat for birds. Tall trees along the length of a hedgerow provide song perches for many birds and a walk along a hedge in the early morning will reveal many of its inhabitants. As expected, those hedges which enclose farmland will support many seed-eating birds, and various finch-like birds are to be found. Due to its 'Little-bit-o-bread-and-no-cheese' song the beautifully plumaged yellowhammer is the most noticeable of these. Much rarer, but occupying a similar habitat, is the cirl bunting; this bird is very much a West Country speciality and can be found along some of the lanes in South Devon. A close look will show the darker facial markings which differentiate the two birds. Although not strictly a hedgerow bird, the closely related corn bunting is worth mentioning here as it is usually found on farmland. A sporadic breeder in Devon, it is much more likely to be encountered in North Cornwall near the coast. The pretty red-chested linnet is spotted far more often than might be imagined and in Cornwall it may nest more frequently than the wren. The wren is a tiny bird with a big voice and its harsh song is to be heard almost everywhere. Mouse-like in its actions, this bird is perfectly at home in the hedgerow as it scurries among the stems and roots looking for the insects which are its prey. More melodious is the whitethroat, a widespread warbler of the more mature hedges and locally called nettle-creeper. This bird sings from the tallest bush in the hedgerow. The base of the hedge provides homes for a variety of birds including the pheasant and the stocky grey partridge, and in South and East Devon especially the red-legged partridge or 'frenchman'. Like the pheasant the red-leg is an introduced bird, but unlike its long-tailed cousin it will probably not be so successful in its spread as it does not settle down well in areas of high rainfall.

Harvest mice at summer nest •

WEASELS

The old adage 'A weasel is easily distinguished and a stoat is totally different' is not a lot of help when one of those small mustelids scampers off into the ditch looking for all the world like a brown stick with legs. Stoat and weasel are both possessed of insatiable curiosity and a wait of a few moments should reward the watcher with a view clear enough to see whether there is a black tip to the tail. If there is, it is a stoat; otherwise it is a weasel. The weasel is the smallest of the British Mustelidae, which include the badger, otter, pine marten and mink, its sharp-toothed skull tiny enough to pass through a wedding ring. Its long, slim, slinky shape is ideal for getting into the tight places among the roots and boulders where its usual prey of voles and mice are to be found. All the mustelids bear musk glands which produce the scents so important in communication with other members of the species, and droppings laced with these are used as territorial markers.

Typical Upright Stance

Dragging Prey

Tracks

Chin Spots

Weasel Skull & Wedding Ring

Weasel Droppings   Stoat

A positive benefit to the farmer was the introduction of the little owl, Britain's smallest resident owl species and one which can be seen in many areas where lowland farming provides the beetles and moths upon which it feeds. Standards and the numerous telephone poles which follow hedges are ideal perches for these small day-flying owls. Raptors also use these look-out posts and buzzards are a common sight on farmland. More spectacular along the lanes are the low-level fighter bombers of the bird world – the sparrowhawks. One of the delights of walking the lanes in the West Country is the sight of one of these highly manoeuvrable predators as it soars through the air below hedge height before sweeping over to pounce on one of the unsuspecting inhabitants of the hedgerow.

The cool shade of woodland on a hot summer's day is not the only reward for venturing into dense undergrowth. Deciduous woodland is one of the most productive habitats for it is here that we see, hear and smell nature in its glorious profusion. After the open days of spring when lowly flowers have striven to grasp the vernal life-giving light after the dark of winter the woodlands close in. Taller herbs clothe the ground and the trees themselves come into leaf. In Devon, Dunsford, Yarner, Wistman's, Dart Valley, Ashclyst and Brownsham, and in Cornwall, Lanhydrock, Peter's, Devichoys, Pelyn and Hawke's are just a few of the woodlands of the region. Some are large and some smaller; some are mixed, though most are deciduous; some are 'ancient' and others more recently managed – each has its own character and is different in detail retaining similar general conditions for wildlife.

Among the trees the persistent cooing of the now plump, ring-necked wood pigeons is mixed with the calls of other birds, many of them hidden from sight by the protective leaves. The drumming of the woodpeckers, declaring their territories against a hollow tree carries through the woodland and it takes a sharp eye to see the bird itself. These birds are superbly adapted for a life among the trees. Their feet have two toes pointing forwards and two backwards to ensure a strong grip, essential for running up and down the trunks of branches as they search for insect prey. As tree-living species the woodpeckers have no rivals. The stout beak is ideal for hammering the bark, the skull with its loosely knit bones absorbs the shock, and the hair-like feathers protect the eyes and nostrils by keeping out flying dust and woodchips. The tail is specially strengthened to provide the third leg of the tripod which braces the bird against the tree and the long barbed tongue is perfect for investigating the winding passages of the bark beetles upon which it feeds. The largest of the woodpeckers is the green woodpecker; the flash of its yellow-green rump as the bird moves from tree to tree on swooping wings makes it noticeable. More of a tapper than a drummer, this bird also has a laughing cry which gives it its country name of 'Yaffle', but be warned for a yaffling woodpecker is also known as the 'rainbird' and the sound is a portent of rain to come. Despite its name the great spotted woodpecker is quite a small bird and is only great in relation to its yet smaller cousin the lesser spotted. Both spotted woodpeckers are black and white and, like the green, have a red head. These are the real drummers and as might be expected the sound of the larger bird is much more audible.

The brown, bark-coloured treecreeper is usually silent during the summer months but it is a common enough bird and almost any woodland walk should reveal it spiralling up one tree trunk before flying to the base of the next tree for another ascent in search of the insects which are also its food. The nuthatch, with slate-blue upper parts and chestnut-washed underparts, is quite able to move up and down as well as sideways on a tree where it, too, hunts for insects in addition to nuts and seeds. Adding their songs to the general chorus are the warblers. Willow warbler and chiff chaff are so similar that many 'birders' record them as 'willow-chiffs' but they give away their identities when they sing and the 'chiff-chaff' call of the one is unmistakable. The woodwarbler more rarely will be heard or seen as it hovers below the leaves where it finds its food.

The real hoverers of the woods are the flycatchers. The spotted flycatcher often gives itself away by having a few favourite perches where its droppings accumulate as a sign that there is some activity to be watched. This little, striped rather than spotted, bird is a delightful species with the most acrobatic of flights. From its perch it keeps a sharp eye open for a passing insect whereupon it darts out, hovering in mid air as it collects its reward. The black and white pied flycatcher is also a regular species in many woodlands where there are holes for nesting and to be sure of sighting this bird it is best to visit woodlands where it has been encouraged. Nest box schemes in Yarner Wood and the woods around Oakhampton in Devon have been successful and the National Trust woodlands at Lanhydrock, too, have been graced with visits from this bird.

The crow of the woodlands is the jay although the flash of blue from the wings and the distinctive white rump are less often seen than the screeching call is heard. Acorns are a favourite food, so oak woodlands are the places to look.

Woodland rides, at night, are the hunting grounds of the tawny owl as it flies with silent wings in search of its prey of woodmouse, field vole and common shrew. The 'tu-whit, tu-whoo' or 'keewick, hoo-hoo' call of the tawny is the owl sound heard most often these days but it indicates not one bird but two. The call is a contact call with a single bird giving the 'keewick' to be answered by the 'hoo-hoo' of its partner, but not necessarily its mate. When prey is captured it is swallowed whole, the bones and fur being regurgitated as a pellet. The pellets are dry and fragile, but a good search below a favourite perch may reveal a pellet or two which has survived the descent through the branches above. Careful dissection exposes the remains of the owl's meal and can give an indication of what small animals are around and available to the bird. During the day the tawny owl's roost may be the centre of attention for the numerous chaffinches, blackbirds, wrens and other small birds which the woodland harbours. Burying their territorial differences in the face of what they see as a joint threat, they mob the sleepy owl in an attempt to dislodge it from its slumbers. Similar 'mobbing' activity can be seen wherever a buzzard or sparrowhawk, both woodland nesters, passes close to a rookery. Like a squadron of black-painted fighters the rooks shoot into the air to harry the passing raptor. The buzzard circles lazily on the thermals until it leaves the irritation behind while the sparrowhawk outflies the mob on its fast wings. All three birds prefer woodlands near farmland where they can hunt their food in open country or along the hedgerows.

Woodlands provide cover for the shy and secretive deer and off the beaten track it is quite common to flush a roe deer from its laying-up place. Early to mid-summer sees the fawns being born, the spotted coat blending perfectly with light-dappled undergrowth in which its mother leaves it while she goes foraging for food. Like baby birds the fawn is not abandoned and under no circumstances should it be 'rescued'; the merest trace of human scent is enough to cause the mother to abandon it. Scent is very important when it comes to watching wildlife for most mammals have acute senses of smell and sniff you out long before you get near them. Where an animal has been spotted you should circle to get the wind in your face before you make a closer approach.

Like most mammals the badger does not rely on a single sense, but takes a reading from its eyes, ears and nose before making a decision. Badgers are still common throughout the region and especially where a combination of tree cover and steep slopes provide ideal conditions for digging and finding food. The badger is a large and powerful animal, but one which is gentle and docile unless molested. An inveterate digger, the badger makes no attempt to hide the whereabouts of its underground fastness, the sett, and heaps of earth around its entrance and exit holes are the first indicator that a particular woodland is home for these, the heaviest, members of the weasel tribe. Even in dusk the black and white striped head is obvious and far from being some form of camouflage is rather a warning that the badger is coming. Rather like the red flag paraded before the first motor cars the badger's colours simply states that a large and powerful animal is about to pass by. It intends no harm and suggests that you move out of its way. Badger-watching, starting an hour before dusk and often continuing for hours into the night is one of the most pleasant of summer activities. Out of respect for the animals you should sit with your back to a tree, or better still up in its branches, so as to make yourself invisible. The breeze should be in your face to take your scent away from the badgers and you should make no sound. Soon the badgers, testing the night air with every available sensor, will emerge. At first maybe only one, the boar, will surface and sit back on his haunches for a good scratch before the whole group emerges. Adults keeping a wary eye, ear and nose open for potential danger begin to scrape for food before moving off for more productive pastures while the young perfect their woodcraft by playing and fighting.

Clean animals, badgers may bring out their bedding for an airing or collect some more afresh. Moving backwards with their front legs dragging a ball of grass or bracken, this is when they are most easily observed. Regular pathways are used and runs in the undergrowth become more and more apparent as the vegetation of summer fills the rest of the woodland floor. Such trackways lead to feeding grounds in a nearby field, for example, where they search for earthworms which have surfaced on a damp summer's night. Badgers' cleanliness stretches to careful disposal of droppings in small excavated hollows called 'dung pits', a source of investigative material for the keener naturalist who wants to find out what badgers eat. Badgers have been described as opportunistic omnivores, which means that they will eat virtually anything they happen to come across. The diet of the badger is dictated to some extent by the weather. Earthworms are an especial favourite if they can be found and it is not uncommon to see large numbers of badgers foraging amongst cowpats on adjoining farmland in search of earthworms. The cowpats themselves are a rich supply of beetles and other insects which come to feed and lay their eggs among the decaying vegetable refuse. A sure sign that badgers are about and that they are to be encouraged is the sight of a dug-out wasps' nest. The thick fur and tough hide of the badger is a useful protection against the angry wasps as they

witness the devouring of their prized grubs. Other small diggings might be seen where badgers have scraped among the bulbs and roots of the woodland floor for other insects as well as the succulent storage organs of the plants.

The large number of plant species in the woodlands make them ideal places for insects. Whether they be nectar hunters, leaf munchers or bark borers the woodland is their home. The nest of the wood ant is probably one of the most familiar objects encountered during a walk through the woods. Huge heaps of woodland refuse appear to have been swept up by a tidy forester, but a close look will show that each fragment of twig or leaf is carefully placed and the whole is covered with a swarm of large ants. The surrounding area is also alive with these busy creatures and if you linger too long you will become an object for inspection, with ants crawling up your legs and testing your edibility with a small nip. A close look at the milling workers should show that some are very definitely moving away from the nest in search of food, whereas others, with a slightly fatter appearance, are making their way back. The latter have been to the feeding grounds where they have milked the aphid herds and are returning to feed the larval ants in the nest. Other food includes various caterpillars and other insects and as many as 100,000 of these might be collected in a single day by the members of a single colony. Wood ants can therefore have a dramatic effect on the local insect population.

Although food is important to a colony of ants not all of its members are engaged in its finding, for there are other jobs to be done. The domed heap over the nest acts as a heat gatherer to incubate the eggs below and like a thatched roof to deflect water from a downpour; inevitably minor maintenance has to be carried out. Many ants will be seen scurrying along carrying twigs or bits of leaf to repair damage and make minor adjustments. Others will be defenders and if you approach too close for the ants' liking you will see them bend their abdomens under and towards you in preparation for a squirt of formic acid. Even if you do not see it you can smell it. Ants have many enemies but perhaps the strangest are the raiding parties of a similar species which storm the nest and head for the breeding grounds. Seizing a hapless cocoon they take it away to their own nest for a life of slavery. Often the ants' nests appear to have suffered from some major catastrophe which has left the carefully constructed 'thatch' in a state of disorder. This is usually the result of a visit from the green woodpecker. Without so much as a tap at the door this bird descends on the nest and spreads its wings wide to allow the annoyed ants among its feathers. It may even help them along by lifting them in its bill and placing them in particular places. This masochistic pastime is called 'anting' and is a normal part of the bird's behaviour. The actual significance is not really understood but it is thought that the ants help clear the bird's feathers of parasites.

Woodland rides are the best places to see the many butterflies which regard the deciduous woods as their natural home. Here the fast flying fritillaries can be seen. The pearl and small pearl bordered fritillaries are the commoner of the

• *Badgers from a sett, on the Two Moors Way, that has been used for decades*

smaller species and may be seen feeding at violets which also provide sustenance for the rarer high brown and the larger silver-washed. Where open woodland with cow wheat and narrow-leaved plantain are found the nationally rare heath fritillary may be encountered. White butterflies do not usually cause much excitement but the delicate, tissue-paper-like wood white is not common and its floppy flight, in early summer, should be regarded as a special sighting. The large, purple-sheened purple emperor is occasionally seen in a few of the more

98 • *Stone-walled animal pens near Candra, Bodmin*

established woodlands in the region but care should always be exercised in identification as it has been confused with the more common white admiral.

Numerous bees visit the woodland blooms and the ever-present wasps find homes among the roots and branches of the trees. The largest of these is the hornet, a formidable-looking but relatively docile wasp of later summer. Hollow trees are ideal places for wasps' nests and the characteristic buzzing should give you plenty of warning to keep away. Many species of wasp are

small and do not carry the yellow or orange and black warning stripes of the bigger species. The majority are unseen by all but the most searching eyes, yet some make themselves very obvious as a result of what they do to some of the woodland plants. The gall wasps are the tiny insects responsible for many of the peculiar growths which adorn trees. They are not the result of disease but are stimulated by an egg being laid in the tissues of the plant. Each species produces a characteristic growth and once identified are relatively easy to distinguish. The oaks support more insects than almost any other species and among the hundreds of species inhabiting the trees are many kinds of gall wasp. Around the acorn cup are the curious knopper galls, while expanded leaf buds produce the artichoke gall, oak apple and marble galls. Leaves support wart galls, oyster galls and spangle galls; other galls are found on the twigs, roots and every part of the tree. Many of these wasps show alteration of generations, where the insects emerging from one kind of gall may produce eggs parthenogenetically (not needing to mate) which when hatched in turn lay eggs giving rise to true mating individuals. The galls themselves provide food for the growing larvae as well as some protection against predators. They do not, however, offer much protection when it comes to some of the parasitic cousins of the gall wasps. The insects find the galls and lay their eggs inside the chambers where the gall wasp larvae are developing and in turn others may lay their eggs on these second larvae. Among the parasites on other insects ichneumon wasps are the most spectacular. These slim-waisted insects can be seen running over the bark of a dead tree in an attempt to detect a beetle or moth larva below. Once one is found, the ichneumon curls its 'tail' and unsheaths its stiletto-like ovipositor which is thrust into the wood until it finds a juicy grub on which an egg is laid.

Dead trees are arguably as useful as live ones and a whole ecological environment lurks below the bark and among the rotting timber. It is an accepted management technique to leave piles of logs and branches on the woodland floor, and you will see this in most nature reserves. The stag beetle is very rare in the West Country but its smaller cousin, the lesser stag beetle, is still a formidable-looking insect and is common among the decaying wood. The piles of brushwood are often frequented by the smaller insectivorous birds, such as wren, great tit and blackcap where they find both nesting sites and a ready supply of food. Here also the hedgehog, more familiar in the towns but really a woodland animal, can be found during the day. At night it is out foraging for its invertebrate food in the more open glades. Woodlice, millipedes, centipedes, slugs and snails and a myriad of other creatures live here as well as in the leaf litter which makes up the forest floor. The annual leaf fall is the first stage in the recycling of valuable nutrients into the soil and it is the multitude of small creatures, bacteria and fungi which continue this recycling process, ensuring that the woods do not die.

FIELD NOTES

AUTUMN

The change from summer to winter is not heralded quite so dramatically in the West Country as in other parts of Britain. Fading trees are often as much a result of drought-like conditions in the summer as they are a preparation for the winter to come. Drawing lines in time between summer and autumn, and autumn and winter, is thus quite difficult to achieve. The fall here is a gradual process and, depending on the harshness of the winter, leaves may still be on trees until well into the new year; hot, dry weather is quite common well into September giving 'Indian summers'. Summer seems to go on for ever and it is not until the first sharp frosts that the leaves give up the battle and drop from the trees to clothe the ground, the ubiquitous bracken browns and curls and the heathers of the moors fade. Dying plants are part of the cycle of nature, rotting down to enhance the richness of the soils and providing a habitat for a myriad of small animals and delicate plants.

However gradual, the advance of nature into the rest period of winter is still inevitable and eventually the trees take on the familiar autumn hues of browns, golds and reds. Most noticeable, in North Devon in particular, are the burnished red copper-coloured hedgerows of neatly trimmed beech, the dense growth providing an impenetrable barrier for livestock, an efficient windbreak and a valuable habitat harbouring a wealth of wildlife. From afar individual trees can be picked out of the masses which cover the steep valleys so typical of Devon and Cornwall as one by one the deciduous species give in to the remorseless approach of autumn and the following winter.

Autumn may be almost at the close of the year but it is a time of plenty and harvest. Nature sets out her stores to tempt a whole host of animals and ensure that the seeds of this year's plants are taken away to grow into the next generation. All through the summer the trees, shrubs and flowers have been soaking up the sun and using it for photosynthesis to produce and sustain growth. The bees and butterflies have been busy visiting the flowers and pollinating the plants, the seeds are set and the productive life of the plants is nearly over for another few months. Autumn is the time of seeds, nuts, fruits

• *The dormouse, soon to leave its summer nest, reaches its peak weight* and berries, and the branches of every hedgerow and tree are bending under the weight of its bounteous produce.

Very early on in the autumn the green frilled nuts of the hazel are starting to harden off and turn brown as they ripen. Many of the birds and mammals will notice this and continue to investigate a bush in the hope that there are some for the picking. Nocturnal mammals, too, will venture from the ground to display their acrobatic skills as they attempt to nip off a likely meal.

As you might imagine the hazel is a tough nut to crack and the way a nut has been opened can tell you which animal has claimed the milky-flavoured reward

• *The Teign Valley under Sharp Tor*

inside. If the nuts are still on the tree and the holes are large and irregular the chances are that they have been eaten by woodpeckers. Most animals take the nuts away to a more stable dining place than the precarious perch they find at the end of a hazel twig and a good place to look for nut fragments is at the base of the tree. Collecting a few of these for close examination will tell you much about the animals which regard the hazel as tasty to eat. Nuts cracked in half are more than likely the work of the strong teeth of the grey squirrel. The wood mouse gnaws from the inside out and so leaves a crumbly-looking hole with a circle of tiny teeth marks; the bank vole uses its upper incisors and gnaws from

the outside, resulting in a much neater hole without the ring of teeth marks. A real prize find is a nut with a very smooth hole which looks as if it has been reamed by an electric drill. This is evidence of the shy and nocturnal dormouse, an animal which is particularly found in the West Country and which inhabits the tangled growth of bramble and honeysuckle so characteristic of the hazel coppice. Interestingly, the majority of dormouse records do not refer to sightings of the animals but to the presence of the nuts opened in this fashion, so if you find one do send it to the relevant County Wildlife Trust who will be pleased to add another dot to their distribution maps and perhaps learn a little more about the life of this elusive rodent. Cracked nuts with heavy beak marks may well be the work of magpies or jackdaws.

A look at the trunk of a nearby tree might reveal opened hazel nuts wedged in the crevices of the bark, the work of birds that have used the tree as an anvil for better purchase before they deliver the hammer blows with their beaks. Small neat holes are the work of the great tit, aptly known as the 'hackmal' in this part of the world, and irregular large holes are produced by the nuthatch.

In all its stages the oak is a tree which is relied on by more animals than any other and this is so in the autumn as well. The acorn crop is a major source of food for a whole variety of animals but it is the birds that are most noticeable and a half hour by a heavily laden tree will be time well spent. A band of blue, flashing jays might descend to strip a tree and take away their gains to be buried for harder times to come. Many of these stores are not found and eaten as acorns, but are left so that they germinate and sprout in the spring, the fresh shoots providing an early and welcome feast. It would be nice to think that the jays were planting seeds for the specific purpose of its new growth but there seems to be little conscious effort and the finding of this source of food is coincidental. Jays in the tree tops might be joined by pheasants on the ground during day-time feeding, but the most surprising acorn feeder is a nocturnal visitor, the mallard. The bird which eats more acorns than any other in the British Isles is the wood pigeon and it has been calculated that one pigeon may eat more than 150 in a day and may hold up to seventy in its crop at any time. The acorn harvest is a glut indeed and in most years there are normally enough to feed all the creatures that require them, leaving a few that escape detection or get buried and forgotten. These are the few that grow into mighty oaks to carry on the line.

In some years, however, the acorn harvest does fail completely and then the rest of nature faces a real threat. Recently a massive infestation of the waxy, brain-like knopper gall, which grows around acorn cups, prevented the nuts from maturing, not just in Britain but on the continent of Europe as well and thousands of jays set off in search of food. Normally seen in small groups, flocks of hundreds were reported from all parts of Britain as they flew in across the channel. Other galls are worth looking out for, especially on the oaks, a tree which has more than its share of insects living on it. Leaves, whether still on the

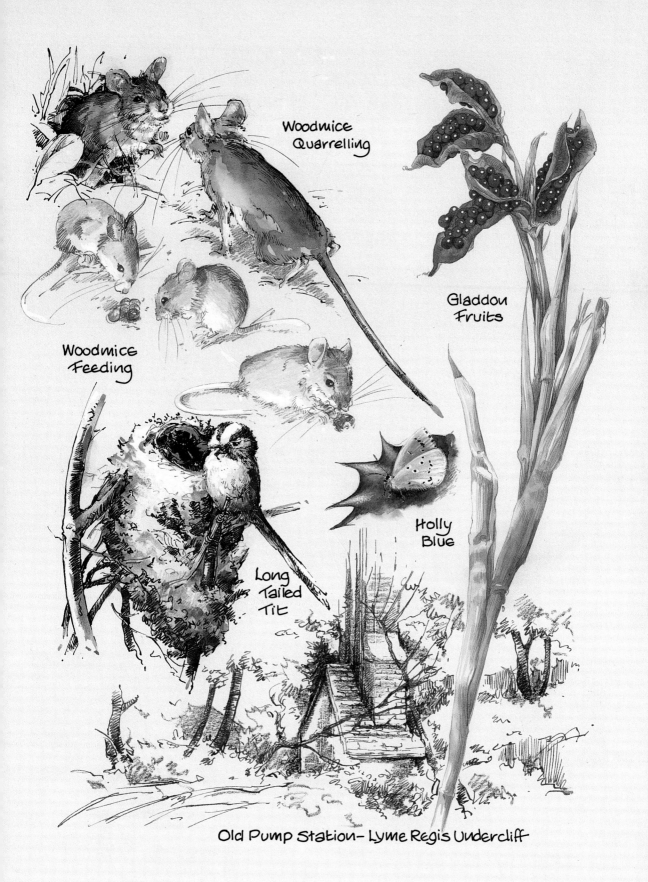

Woodmice Quarrelling

Gladdon Fruits

Woodmice Feeding

Holly Blue

Long Tailed Tit

Old Pump Station- Lyme Regis Undercliff

trees or lying on the ground, will show the tiny cup, smooth and silk-button spangle galls and cherry galls and the remains of the oak apples and marble galls become more obvious as the trees are stripped of their leaves as autumn progresses into winter.

The two chestnut species, although not closely related, protect their nuts by means of prickly outer skins. The conker of the horse chestnut is thought worth the effort of collecting by schoolchildren, while the sweet chestnut is much sought after by 'Sunday afternooners' out on a stroll in the countryside. The sweet chestnut is thought to be a tree introduced by the Romans for its food value and in some years it does repay sorely spiked fingers by giving a good crop of decent-sized nuts.

Many seeds are adapted to be taken away from the parent plant by the gusty autumn winds. Poppies growing in the fields or roadside verges have a seed case rather like a pepper shaker and the tiny black seeds are spread with a hissing rattle every time the breeze moves the stem. Thistle and dandelion have seeds which are equipped with a feathery parachute to be wafted for miles on the slightest whisper of the wind. One plant even changes its name at the turn of the year; throughout the summer the white flowers of the wild clematis have been many a 'traveller's joy' and as the autumn progresses more and more long feathery seeds are formed until the plant truly resembles an 'old man's beard'. The wild clematis is well suited to the warmer conditions of the West Country and can be seen along many hedgerows, especially those on the lime-rich areas of East Devon.

As far as the ash tree is concerned each seed is individually wrapped and fitted with its own sail. As the leaves fall the clusters of green keys begin to dry and darken until, if they have escaped the attention of the bullfinches, they are ready to make their journey to earth. Once caught by the wind the slightly twisted wing ensures that they do not fall direct but spiral down slowly and always end up a good distance from the parent tree. A double-bladed key bearing two seeds has probably come from a nearby sycamore, a tree which though introduced into Britain has proliferated in many woods where it is regarded as something of a pest by those who manage woodlands.

While many of the nuts and seeds are carried by the wind or rely on their smooth surfaces for rolling to a new site for colonisation other plants have seeds which are more likely to be carried further away. The cleavers or goose grass lies in wait for any passing animal, when the barbed seeds play their part by becoming entangled in hair or fur as a means of being transported to pastures new. Other plants produce brightly coloured berries as an enticement for hungry birds and as autumn takes over from summer the woods and hedgerows become a blaze of colour as the various trees and shrubs vie with each other for attention.

Not all shrubs produce their wares at the same time and nature in her infinite wisdom spaces out the fruiting of the different plants and in some cases

GALLS

Nearly all parts of plants can be affected by the curious growths known as galls. Often caused by tiny wasp-like insects, each gall has a characteristic size, shape, colour and position on the plant which make for easy identification. Gall wasps lay their eggs in the plant tissue; as the egg hatches and the larvae develop.

accelerated growth of that part of the plant takes place, providing an ever-expanding food source and shelter for the grub at the same time. Among the more noticeable galls are robin's pin-cushion; its tangled green and red mossy growth is unmistakable on the wild rose. The longer-established native plants tend to have more types of galls than others and the oak, as expected, shows a wide variety. Buds are swollen into 'artichokes', 'apples' and 'marbles', the underside of the leaves bearing the tiny button-like 'spangles' and the acorn cup may be transformed into the strange waxy, brain-like 'knopper'.

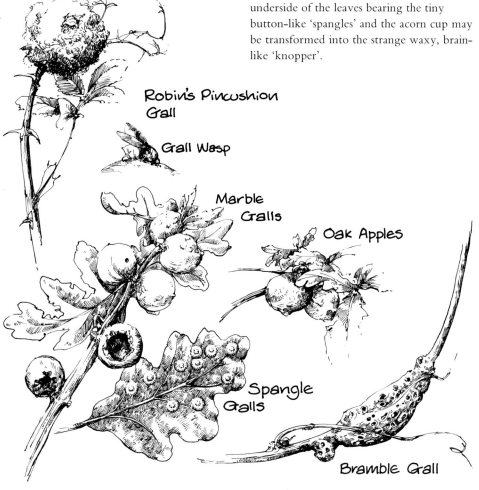

Robin's Pincushion Gall

Gall Wasp

Marble Galls

Oak Apples

Spangle Galls

Bramble Gall

individual fruits on a single shrub so as to give the maximum benefit for the
birds which feed on them. The benefit is not all geared towards the birds,
however, for the berries bear the seeds of the next generation. If these seeds are
to be distributed into new areas there is no point in them all being ready at the
same time as most would fall at the roots of their parent plant and be wasted.

Blackberries are among the first fruits to ripen and tempt the palates of
visiting birds. Any blackberry picker cannot fail to notice that there seem to be

110   • *Honeysuckle and snail in a churchyard near Sancreed*

as many different types of blackberry as there are bushes to be picked over. The fruits vary in size, taste and texture. Some are more prickly than others, some have larger leaves. The number of 'varieties' seems to change each year but it is safe to assume that the humble bramble is in fact a very complex group of plants, distinguishable into something like 350 varieties. The backward-pointing thorns are typical of a climber and indeed the bramble is very efficient when it comes to directing its leaves towards the sun, advertising its fruit in the

Fuchsia

Pedunculate Oak

Sessile Oak

Guelder Rose

Rowan

Field Voles

Sloe

Honeysuckle

open for the birds as the scrambling bramble twists and twines on its upward journey. As a plant the bramble is almost as interesting as the oak tree as regards the diversity of wildlife that lives in and on it. Lazy autumn wasps are a hazard to the picker as they vie for the succulent fruity harvest. The leaves are food for a variety of creatures and many a bramble patch has its own population of rabbits and the foxes which hunt them. A few hours observing a bramble thicket when in full fruit is time well spent. This should not be difficult as they are one of the most invasive of plants, and occur in all parts of the West Country. Another early fruiter is the elder and the warm climate of the region ensures a good crop in most years, trees bending with the weight of black berries which are eagerly consumed by a host of small birds.

The red berries of the hawthorn and the rowan are a distinctive feature of the region. As far as the rowan is concerned the birds seem to forget their differences and a favourite tree is alive with all of the blackbirds in an area. Clinging to the more substantial twigs the birds defy gravity as they balance precariously within beak reach of their reward. A close look at a clump of berries shows that the birds are quite methodical in their approach, working inwards to the centre.

This first glut of fruit is nature's loss leader and ensures that the avian shoppers gain a good start for the harder times to come. Most hedges contain at least one rose bush laden with succulent hips to tempt the seed dispersers. When ripe the hips are without equal as a source of food and attract not just the fruit-eating birds and insects but some of the mammals as well. The uncommon dormouse, and the more frequently seen wood mouse both feed on hips. A red hip is not necessarily ripe and when in this first stage can be quite tough skinned and ignored by the majority of birds. Birds will investigate the bush until they find the one or two hips which are truly ripe. As the fruits become palatable a few at a time the birds will come back over and over again, thus ensuring that the seeds are spread into a variety of different places.

Although usually associated with Christmas the holly, too, will fruit in the autumn, but while the berries appear to be ripe they are apparently distasteful to many birds at this stage. If other fruits are available the holly is left alone but if it is the only berry bearer in the vicinity the birds have little choice. As autumn progresses into winter and the shelves of nature's larder become bare so the holly is all that is left.

Other fruits of a different sort are best seen at this time of year – fungi. Since they are neither green nor rely on light for life but grow out of the death and decay of other plants and animals fungi are surrounded by myth and legend at worst and suspicion at best. The British are generally regarded as strange by our continental cousins for the lack of understanding we show towards this group of odd plants, a group which is both fascinating and nutritious. It is true that a certain amount of caution has to be exercised if one wants to become a fungal gourmet, but these days there is little excuse for the not finding out. There are

• *Hedgerow species, Helston in early October*

now many good books available to help in your identifications and every year at the beginning of the autumn natural history societies and Wildlife Trusts organise a whole range of fungal forays led by experts, intended for learners. The toadstools, mushrooms and bracket fungi we see can really be regarded as autumn fruits as they are the part of the plant which bears the millions of spores waiting to be let loose to start the next generation. The plant itself is a fairly insignificant-looking collection of fine tubes which grow in a mat-like mass under the surface of the soil, beneath the fallen leaves or under the bark of trees. Only when the conditions are right, usually a warm wet summer and a mild autumn, do the fruits push up towards the air where we can see them. Even so, a

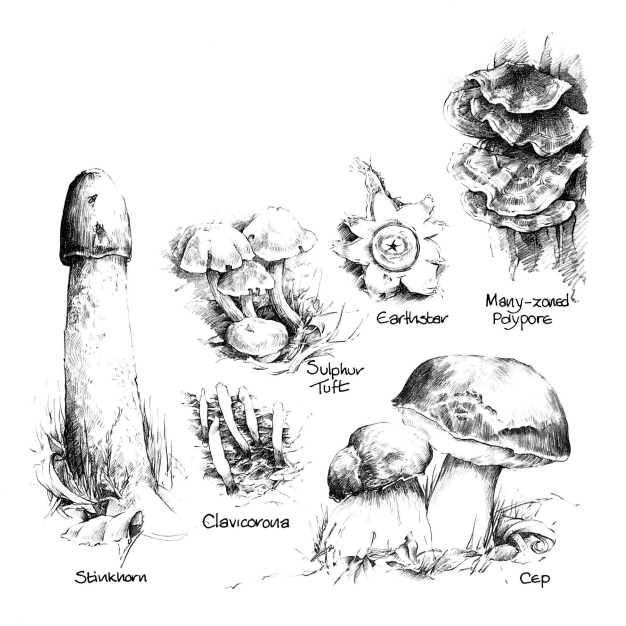

Stinkhorn

Sulphur Tuft

Clavicorona

Earthstar

Many-zoned Polypore

Cep

keen eye is necessary to spot some of them but careful searching in almost any habitat should be amply rewarded by a treat for the senses. Some are quite bizarre in shape, colour and habit and, of course, some are a delight to eat. The sheltered valley woodlands of Devon and Cornwall are especially suitable for fungi but they can be found in virtually every habitat, including even fairly high moorland.

One of the most common and striking fungi of our woodlands is the fly agaric. The bright red cap flecked wth white spots is immediately obvious among the autumn hues of the forest floor. Its red and white colour is associated with legends of Father Christmas and his flying reindeer; as the species is highly hallucinogenic, causing reindeer and their attendant Lapps to leap about as if they could fly, the species is regarded as poisonous. It is often stated that if a fungus is eaten by insects or other animals then it is safe for humans to eat too. Many agaric fungi will be seen to have pieces nibbled out of them and grubs living in them and certainly in these cases it is better to be safe than sorry and avoid them unless you have the benefit of the experience of an expert. Other poisonous members of the agaric group are the destroying angel and the death cap – the most lethal fungus known and one which has no known antidote. Admittedly these two species are not as common in deciduous woodlands as some other species but their occasional presence should be looked out for, if only so that you know what to avoid.

When it comes to searching for the yellow-stainer colour comes to the rescue. This fungus belongs to the same group as the more familiar mushroom and does not look dissimilar, but its habit of producing a bright chrome-yellow stain when cut or bruised tells you that it is no ordinary mushroom – just as well as it is a poisonous species. Likewise the blusher, one of the edible amanitas – but only if cooked properly – becomes tinged with pink on exposure to air.

Boletus species are some of the more sought after fungi. Not all of them are edible but those that are, are said to be well worth getting to know and their flesh is described as excellent. Unlike the usual toadstool the boletes do not have fine gills on the undersurface of the cap, but instead spongy tissue, each of the tubes containing the spores.

Some fungi may not be poisonous to humans but they can cause considerable damage if they begin to grow on a living tree. The honey fungus has been described as the most destructive of our fungi and masses of its golden-yellow toadstools can often be seen growing around an old tree stump or the base of a living tree in deciduous as well as coniferous woodlands.

Many species may be found living in a variety of habitats but one often found on the edges of the old Scots pine stands especially in East Devon is the aptly named cauliflower fungus, a species which is edible but has to be picked before it gets too large otherwise it is impossible to get the tightly packed lobes of the 'flower' clean. A variety of fungi, including some of the bright cup-fungi, can be found in the conifer plantations and at least in autumn give the otherwise

• *The broadleaved woodlands of South Devon are rich in fungi*

barren ground a splash of colour and interest. Shaggy ink cap is a species which seems to grow almost everywhere, even in the sand on bare dunes.

A fungus which is easy to find is the stinkhorn and, as its name implies, it is the sense of smell rather than sight which draws your attention first, although it does have a distinctive and memorable shape, being phallus-shaped, hence its scientific name of *Phallus impudicus*. In its early stages of development it resembles a small egg filled with jelly which is to be found by searching beneath the layer of leaf litter.

Often found on pasture land as well as in the woodlands is another ball-shaped fungus, equally distinct because of its size. The giant puffball can attain a diameter of 80 cm and where it occurs in numbers has often been mistaken for sheep, either dead or resting. It has a smooth skin and when fresh a firm flesh; tapping with the fingers will produce a sound which reflects its solid nature. This species is quite good to eat as long as the flesh is still firm. It can be sliced or stuffed with onions and baked. As a puffball ages it becomes brown and leathery and eventually collapses to release its spores, up to seven billion of them.

The method of growth of fungi is such that the underground body of the plant – the mycelium – grows outwards from a central point extracting essential nutrients from the soil. As it does so it pushes outwards in a circular manner, fruiting around the perimeter. If no opposition is met, by an obstacle or another fungus growing from another direction a 'fairy ring' may be formed. 'Fairy rings' are quite common and may continue to grow for a number of years and can be seen to best advantage in grassland which is grazed. Perhaps the best-known example of the fairy ring producer is the 'fairy ring champignon', a delicate and common toadstool, but many other species, including the field mushroom will produce a ring if given the chance.

The clear sharp light of an early morning autumn sun is ideal for showing up one of the most spectacular sights of the West Country. As the slanting rays of the post-dawn sun finger their way across the landscape the hills and valley are shown in high relief. Here and there the odd silver thread glints in the illuminating shafts, and pools of argent appear on the low-lying fields and heaths as the dew they have attracted is lit by the first light of day. Every woodland ride is criss-crossed with metallic threads and the early morning naturalist is soon covered with the delicate silks of autumn spiders. The warm days and cold nights of autumn provide the ideal conditions for the spiders which ride the rising currents. 'Ballooning' is a common method of dispersal for spiders and it is only when they do this *en masse* carrying their trailing threads with them that some appreciation of the number of spiders lurking in the undergrowth can be realised. When faced with a gossamer-festooned field, hedge or wood it is easy to believe the unbelievable – that there may be as many as two million spiders to .5 hectares, half of which have taken to the air. Gossamer is best seen in late autumn, interestingly enough at the time of the Goose Fairs and it is likely that the two events are connected, at least in name.

DORMICE

The dormouse is one of the few mammals to hibernate and is one of our more elusive creatures although it may be more common than sightings would indicate. A nocturnal creature of dense thickets where hazel, bramble and honeysuckle predominate, it is usually only seen when disturbed from its ball-like nest, where it has been curled up asleep. The small size, orange colour, large eyes and furry tail distinguish it from all other mice, but its presence is often only indicated by the characteristic tooth-marks it leaves on hazelnuts. Any hazel coppice in Devon and Cornwall is worth a second look to find the dormouse.

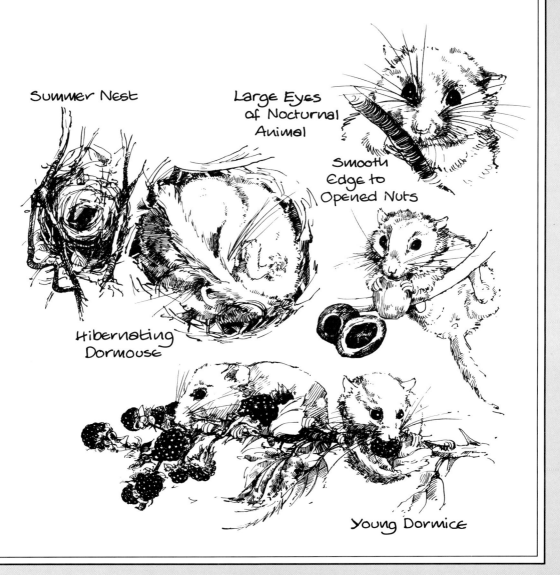

Summer Nest

Large Eyes of Nocturnal Animal

Smooth Edge to Opened Nuts

Hibernating Dormouse

Young Dormice

Gossamer is thought to be a contraction of 'Goose Summer', itself a reference to the feather-like spider silk, the warm weather and the Goose Fairs.

Larger spiders, like the orb-weavers, will not last the winter and the gravid females have a last feast before they lay their eggs and die. It is probably just as well that autumn is a time when many insects are about for them to feed on. September and October are noted in the West Country as the two months when craneflies appear in their thousands. Those most noticeable are the larger species which can be found where there is grass – the larvae, the leather jackets, feed on the roots. With 300 species in this country they can be found in almost any habitat as they rise from the ground for their nuptial flights. The cooling conditions of autumn means that many insects are coming to the end of their adult lives. Some lay their eggs and die, others in the form of larvae or adults may search out a hibernation site. Warm periods during the winter are sufficient to reinvigorate many of these and clouds of midges may be found dancing in shafts of sunlight. Late butterflies are still on the wing and fallen fruit in orchards prove a magnet to the migrant red admiral; clouds of these can be found wherever there is rotting fruit to tempt them. Drowsy wasps, too, visit fruit as if the fermenting apples could perk them up for winter but most of these are doomed to die leaving only queens to crawl away to some crevice for hibernation . Any growth of ivy is well worth watching for it is the last line on offer in nature's floral larder. With little else to feed on, the late insects find a feast at ivy, so on a warm day it is abuzz with activity as bees, hoverflies, wasps and a host of others drop in for a nectar meal. A very sharp eye might just pick out the caterpillars of the holly blue butterfly; this butterfly is double brooded, with the early caterpillars feeding on their namesake plant and the autumn brood finding food and shelter in the foliage of the ivy.

Early evening, especially by the coast, resounds to the chirping of the bush-crickets. Both dark and the great green bush cricket can be heard well into November, only ceasing when the hard frosts finally slow them to the point of death and only their eggs are left to take them through to the next warm season. The occasional dragonfly may also last into the year's third quarter and so even the exposed moorland bogs might have the odd autumn jewel flitting past to brighten up the gradually fading vegetation of summer.

As insects prepare for the winter sleep, and the days draw in, so the birds are readying themselves for the cold, dark days ahead. The departure of the birds of summer seems to be a quiet affair and birds which have brightened up the woods or heaths just seem to fade away. The cuckoo is one of the first to arrive and after a short stay of just four months or so it is one of the first to leave. As the old song says 'July she must fly, August go she must' and with her goes the summer. Equally, even though one swallow does not make a summer a lack of swallows indicates that autumn is on its way. The adult cuckoos leave first, followed by the young of the year a month or so later to embark on a miraculous journey of which they have no knowledge. The fact that the parents foster out their young means that they do not have to linger to see them fledged and ready to face the world. Not so the swifts; acutely aware of the diminishing supply of insects high in the air and the ever-shortening days they start to leave around the middle of August. The departure of the swifts is marked not so much by them not being seen but by the peace that fills the air. The summer-long screeching as these aerobatic birds scythe through the sky is gone for another year. Birds with which we have become familiar are all of a sudden gone from the places we are used to seeing them in. The nightjars no longer churr on the heaths, grasshopper warblers 'reel' no more in the reed beds, flycatcher perches are deserted. By October the migration to warmer climes is in full swing and masses of swallows and house martins line up along every telephone wire. After what appear to be a few practice flights a whole group shoots into the sky and disappears in the direction of the sea. Groups come together to form huge flocks, but still they may not leave British shores completely until they judge conditions to be just right. Sweeping over rivers they drop as one into a reed bed to roost overnight, giving credence to the old belief that they used to dive into mud and hibernate there for the winter. Eventually some signal tells them that it is time to go and off they fly towards the sea and towards the warmer climate of Africa. Many of these migrating birds follow a south-westerly flight path and so it is not surprising that they end up on the various headlands which represent the last land before the first hop across the sea.

All along the south coast of Devon and Cornwall every headland attracts birdwatchers keen to gain a sighting of the moving flocks or a chance rarity resting at the water's edge waiting for weather conditions that favour a good flight. Misty weather and storms keep the birds grounded and make life easier for the keen birdwatcher. Almost any headland facing south is a good place to watch for migrants, but Start and Prawle Points in the South Hams of Devon, and The Lizard and Land's End in Cornwall are particularly worth a visit.

Fellow birdwatchers will be happy to swap notes with you and point you in the direction of the bush, tree or field which holds the 'day's speciality'. Warblers, flycatchers, wheatears, skylarks, wagtails, firecrests and mixed flocks of hundreds of finches flow over the headlands on the first stages of their journeys to warmer climes. On a good day thousands of birds may be seen flying out to sea. Overhead birds of prey may also be spotted. Merlin and peregrine are attracted by the unusual concentrations of birds in such a small area where pickings are easier. A kill can often result in mixed emotions for the birder. Which is more exciting to witness, the arrival of a rare warbler or its death in the talons of a spectacular bird of prey?

No two days are the same on these headlands, every new arrival being announced by a flurry of activity among the dedicated watchers. The autumn migration depends to a certain extent on weather conditions and not all of the birds leave at the same time, so repeat visits will not be in vain. Almost any time between the latter part of August and November will reveal some species of interest. The list seems endless and a few days' migrant watching certainly sharpens your birdwatching skills to pick out the different warblers and finches as they descend to rest for a few moments before erupting in a swirl of wings.

Some of these headlands are busier than international airports for not only can you see thousands of birds waiting for departure but you can also witness the incoming flights of autumn and winter visitors. Autumn is the season of change and the changeover; just as some birds leave us, others which find our climate suitable join us from the north. Among the first, and most spectacular, of these are the redwings and fieldfares. Both species are thrushes flying in from Scandinavia to make a feast on berries. Mixed in with the flocks are other species of thrush such as blackbirds which fly in to bolster the resident population. Soon after arrival the flocks move inland as if to replace the less hardy birds which have left Britain for the winter and before long every field seems to be alive with the sight and sounds of them.

While the bird world is in a state of hyperactivity most of the mammals are going about their business in a more secretive way. Not all British animals hibernate during the cold weather but those that do are getting themselves ready for the long sleep. Dormice have feasted on the autumn harvest, leaving only the shells of hazelnuts to tell the tale. Hedgehogs are still out and about until the weather gets really bad, stocking up their fat layers to keep them going through the days of lack.

For most wildlife autumn is a period of winding down before the cold of winter sets in. Some die off, leaving only the eggs or seeds, while others fly south or hibernate. For a few creatures, however, autumn is the time for replenishment and starting anew. Britain is home to seven of the 36 species of deer, but only two of these are native – the majestic red and the elusive roe. In Devon and Cornwall five of the species can be seen, if you are lucky. The red deer is the famous 'Monarch of the Glen' and while Scotland is a particular stronghold they can be seen elsewhere; in the West Country the main place to look is Exmoor. From the Exmoor nucleus they are spreading out and are now a regular sight on Dartmoor and in some forests around Bodmin. Occasional sightings are seen elsewhere, such as the peculiar occurrence of a full-grown stag swimming the River Exe and the Exeter Canal, well within the city boundary, and then heading west in the direction of Haldon Forest, where a small group are a regular sight, though not resident.

The red deer is Britain's largest native deer; the stags standing at about 1.2 m at the shoulder, while the hinds are slightly smaller. The roe deer is a much smaller animal at only about 75 cm. Different species of deer can be distinguished by height, colour, habitat, the pattern on the rump which is so essential in communication between deer and, of course, the shape of the antlers. It is only the males that bear antlers and unlike horns they are shed and regrown each year. They are used in the breeding season to establish dominance

Red deer compete for hinds on Exmoor in October •

and the clashing of antlers between two stags is more a demonstration of strength than aggression. The growth of antlers is controlled by hormones and when antlers have reached the correct size, determined by the carrying capacity of the deer, the hormone supply is cut off and the antlers begin to die and harden. In the first stage of this process the velvet covering peels away and is rubbed off. This is an uncomfortable stage for the deer and they thrash around in bushes and can do considerable damage to trees in their attempts to get rid of the irritating velvet. This fraying takes place just before the rutting season and can provide a good indicator of where deer might be found. The dying-off process of the antlers is progressive, slowly creeping down towards the skull. If the antlers are not shed the dying-back attacks the skull and could be fatal, so they are cast before death occurs. This might seem a terrible waste but the antlers are recycled by the deer – they are rich in calcium and they are normally eaten, not all in one go but nibbled at from time to time.

The antlers of the red deer are broadly spreading and bear many branches or tines. The number of these can tell you the approximate age of the deer, with a new one appearing each time the antlers are grown. In hunting terms stags are described by the number of points on the antlers. Twelve points is a Royal while an Imperial has fourteen. Antler growth is not always consistent and a stag without points and only a long antelope-like horn is known as a switch and is a particularly dangerous opponent. Occasionally the stags do not develop antlers at all and they are then known as a hummel or humble.

Antler growth in the roe deer is not as spectacular and in keeping with its size; the antlers are mere prongs with only a few points. The rut is equally unimpressive and consists of the male chasing the doe in circles around a particular tree or clump of bushes resulting in a worn ring in the earth – a clue to their whereabouts.

The fallow was the first deer to be introduced into Britain, probably around the time of the Bronze Age. It is the deer usually kept in parks and is the most familiar of our species. The characteristic antlers, flattened and palm-like, are unmistakable. Deer are difficult animals to contain and so high fences are constructed to keep them confined, but the fallow can clear 1.8 m at a bound. Thus many of them have gained their freedom from parks, forming over the years the core of the wild animals which we occasionally see in our woodlands or grazing the fields. Many introductions are mistakes but with deer there have been a lot deliberate liberations. Sika deer, halfway between the red and the fallow in size and appearance were released here from Japan and are in direct competition with red deer with which they also breed, producing hybrids. Although not common they are now found in Devon and if not yet established in Cornwall they soon will be. The tiny and secretive muntjacs and Chinese water deer seem to be harmless, but they are spreading within the West Country and are particularly found in the dense woodlands of the upper Exe Valley beyond Tiverton.

Deer have always been regarded as valued beasts of the chase and as such became royal animals. Special areas were set aside for them, the Royal Forest described as the 'secret places of Kings and their delights'. These sometimes covered huge areas and were not always tree-covered areas as the word today implies. Two of the best known are the New Forest and the West Country's Dartmoor Forest. William the Conqueror was responsible for this and while he did not have time to enjoy hunting in all of his forests he delegated his rights to his lords. Woe betide a commoner who took a deer; his life would be forfeit. Even to shoot at and miss a deer was a crime and resulted in the criminal's hands being cut off. Deer hunting has a long history and is still carried on today, although it is not an exclusively royal prerogative. The subject of hunting is an extremely emotive one. One the one hand the anti-hunt lobby deplores the barbarity it sees in the chase, while huntsmen point out that deer need to be controlled as they do make quite serious inroads into crops and forestry plantations. There is an argument that without hunting to offer some 'entertainment' in return for their continued existence deer would not be tolerated and would have been eradicated long ago. There can be little doubt that this is a fact, although it is an argument that has less support now that there is greater sympathy for wildlife. Red deer continue to play a major role in the life and tradition of Exmoor and stag hunts still take place.

Although all the species of deer differ in their habits to some extent, most of them follow a similar annual pattern. The high spot of the year and the time when deer are most in evidence is the rut. The stags are at their finest during this courtship routine where the males establish their dominance over other males and gather together a harem of females or, in the case of the roe deer, establish a pair relationship. Vocal challenges between males shatter the peace of autumn as the normally quiet stags roar or bark at each other from a distance. If neither challenger nor challenged retreat, contact may be made and the antlers become interlocked. The contest is not usually violent but is more a test of strength so injuries do not necessarily follow. This is nature's way of ensuring the survival of the fittest line. A word of caution, however it is very tempting to approach deer closely when they are otherwise occupied with the rut but there are cases where people have found themselves unwittingly involved presumably on the principle that all is fair in love and war, and a human intruder is considered another challenger. Red deer may be seen along the skyline as magnificent silhouettes at this time of year. Certainly they blend perfectly into the browns of autumn moorland. The steep Exmoor valleys, typical Lorna Doone country, are always worth searching for the odd family party at rest, browsing or drinking from the sparkling streams. Crouched below the crest of the valley side you may well remain unnoticed if you are out of sight, hearing and smell, for deer are acute in all these senses.

After the excitement is over and mating has taken place, the territories break down and stags and hinds form into herds for the winter. In the spring the antlers are cast, and the young are born in the early summer when the dappled sunlight filtering through the undergrowth gives perfect camouflage for the calfs, fawns and kids at rest where they have been left by their mother as she goes off foraging.

It is not often that Britain can make the boast that it has a large percentage of the world population of any creature but this is true of the grey seal. About half of the 200,000 grey seals in the world occur in British waters and of these nearly 2 per cent live off the north coast of Devon and Cornwall, and in the Bristol Channel. Grey seals are a common sight for fisherman and sailors travelling these waters and there are some well-known, if inaccessible, coves where they haul out to give birth to their pups. The coast of North Cornwall is the best place to see these animals as they haul themselves ashore to have their young during September and October, much earlier than in other colonies in this country. Gunver, Trevose and St Agnes Heads are all well-known haul-out places, but the caves and sheltered coves of the Kynance and Lizard Peninsulas should not be missed. From virtually any cliff overlooking the sea along this coast seals are likely to be seen, swimming with perfect ease. Their bodies may be clumsy on land but ideally suit a marine environment. Insatiably curious, seals out of harm's way will float upright in the water taking as much interest in you as you are in them – this is known as 'bottling'.

Towards the end of the summer the first signs that the season is about to be under way is that the seals gather around their favourite coves before coming ashore, almost as if they are spying out the lay of the land before committing themselves. Males will establish a territory on a stretch of beach which they defend against all challengers. The territory is actually chosen by the females who know where they want to have their pups, while the male defends their right to stay in the group. A great deal of huffing and puffing takes place as the unwieldy creatures scramble over the shore to worry away all comers from their harem of up to ten females. Often the contest is just noisy as the males exchange threats, but when two large males meet the fighting can be vicious and sometimes blood is spilt. The males are not simply protecting the females and young, however, but are also waiting for the females to finish suckling their young. It is at this time that the cows once more become receptive to the bulls and mating takes place.

Pupping may occur from a day to a week after the initial hauling out and the pup will have had its first feed within six hours, finding its way to the mother's nipple with the help of a coaxing flipper. The mother's milk is about 60 per cent fat and within a week the white-coated pup will have doubled its weight. After almost three weeks of feeding on the rich milk produced by its mother a pup will have trebled its original birth weight to something like 45 kg and is an appealing barrel-shaped creature. As soon as suckling is finished the young seals are left to their own devices and the adults mate again. The early stages of life for any creature are fraught with dangers and it is no different for the seal, with a third of the young failing to reach their first birthday. It is inquisitive youngsters which are most likely to stray onto the beaches and up the estuaries of the south coast of Devon. Here they receive a mixed welcome depending on whether the observer is a fisherman or a naturalist. The grey seal is the common seal of the West Country but occasional snub-nosed common seals do turn up now and again.

Whilst seals are the most likely mammals to be seen from the cliff tops around Devon and Cornwall, a chance sighting of a whale, porpoise or dolphin should not really be a surprise for cetaceans are regular, if somewhat elusive, visitors to the British Isles. To many people whales are synonymous with leviathans crashing up through polar ice or basking at the surface in the warm waters of the Gulf of Mexico, but we have our fair share of these wonderful creatures and they are worth keeping an eye open for.

Amazingly, more than a quarter of the world's 76 species of cetaceans have been recorded in British waters, and of these eighteen have been spotted, stranded or caught around the coasts of the West Country. One of the more familiar whales, due to its constant appearance on television, is the California grey whale, a species known in the West Country from a few bones found in Devon and Cornwall, evidence of a population which once thrived in the Atlantic and arguably one of the first casualties of exploitation by humans. This species is now restricted to the Pacific Ocean where its lengthy coastal migrations are now well known, but sadly we will never again witness the like along our shores. Large concentrations of cetaceans in the waters around the West Country are now restricted to the schools of porpoise and occasionally dolphins which thrill the lucky coast watcher who happens to be in the right place at the right time. Predicting sightings is virtually impossible and they can be seen almost anywhere along the coast throughout the year, although records show that autumn is the best time and that the South Hams and the east and north coasts of Devon, and Land's End in Cornwall are more prone to sightings than other places. This may, of course, be a reflection of the popularity of these areas for walking but there is some evidence to show that the flotillas of jellyfish which appear throughout the summer and early autumn are attractive to some species of cetaceans as a source of food and that as far as strandings are concerned the currents in these places are more conducive to cetaceans being washed up than in other areas.

The smallest of our cetacean visitors are the porpoises which follow shoals of fish along the coast. At a maximum length of 1.8 metres, and lacking a pronounced 'beak' they are also the easiest to identify. At the other end of the scale, the giant 'finners', or rorquals, can attain a length of 25 metres and truly deserve the title of 'monster of the deep' with which they are greeted by local journalists whenever they have the misfortune to come ashore.

Identification of cetaceans at sea is notoriously difficult and is not helped by the infrequency of sightings. If a cetacean happens to be stranded, the story can be quite different, and sad though the sight of a dead whale is, it can still be a source of knowledge and the discovery of any cetacean should be reported to the local Coast Guard who will make arrangements for its identification, measurement and disposal. Most cetaceans are 'royal fish' and technically belong to the Crown – the Customs and Excise being the agents.

The pilot whale or blackfish, which may be 6 metres in length, is one of the commoner species to be found on the strandline and indeed it is this species which is most often seen to 'beach' in large groups or pods. Why they do this, especially when most of the herd are still alive and seem to be perfectly healthy, remains one of the unanswered questions of nature, but it may be a communal response to one of their number suffering an illness or injury seeking sanctuary in shallow water and the rest following, not wanting to abandon it.

Perhaps the most familiar of all cetaceans is the Orca (recent research shows that the term killer whale is quite unjustified as far as humans are concerned). Pods of these black and white, tall-finned, toothed whales are a regular sight in the Channel and around Lundy off the north Coast of Devon.

Sightings of cetaceans should always be recorded meticulously. You should note at least the date, time and direction of travel. If you can, include the size, the colour, the shape of the tail-fluke and dorsal fin, the number of individuals and any other observations on behaviour. We still know surprisingly little about these animals on a world-wide basis and even less about their activities around our own coasts. Any information, however little, can be a great help in increasing our knowledge and encouraging conservation of these enigmatic denizens of the deep.

FIELD NOTES

WINTER

S now is rare in the counties of Devon and Cornwall but when it does occur it can provide a real insight into the lives of some of our mammals and birds. Tracks in the snow are a giveaway of activity from the previous night and an early start before the thaw sets in or the tracks are obscured can reveal much about the lives of these secretive animals. Frozen ponds and rivers with a sprinkling of dusty whiteness show where an otter has been, although increasingly the tracks you see are more likely to be those of the introduced North American mink. Bends in rivers are good places to look for the prints of otters as they often leave the water to take a short cut. Their favourite food is frequently brought out of the water and there may be some remnants of the meal to help you decide exactly what it is you are looking at. A half-eaten eel with webbed, five-toad prints points to the presence of the otherwise careful otter. Waterbirds too will leave their tracks and the large three-toed print of the heron shows where this sentinel of the river bank has stood waiting for a chance fish or water vole to come within stabbing distance. Moorhen and coot often feed on land and leave their characteristics signatures in the form of footprints on water meadows.

Following tracks for any distance can be a bit of a problem near water as the animals seem to cover their tracks at every opportunity by going back into the water, crossing sides and doubling back on themselves. Snow covered fields are a better bet, where the numerous prints of the ubiquitous rabbit are plain to see. Groups of two small prints in front of each other, for the forefeet, and in front of them two longer ones, side by side for the hindfeet, are pressed into the snow as the rabbit hops along. The only real difference in prints from those of the hare is their size. Hedgerows are the natural hiding places of rabbits and so the tracks tend to be concentrated along them. It is also here that you should look for the tracks of their predators. The stoat is another mammal which does not hibernate and is very difficult to spot during the summer months when there is plenty of vegetation to hide it. In winter with snow on the ground the stoat cannot help but give the clues which many naturalists rely on to gain some idea of the home range of these animals. An animal that jumps its way through life,

• *Fox watching from its earth under a tor, Dartmoor*

and the snow, the tracks are grouped a little like those of the hare or rabbit, but on a much smaller scale and the five toes and claw marks may often be seen. Further north in Britain the stoat often assumes its winter coat of ermine, but in the West Country pure white stoats are very rare indeed. Occasional partial ermine have been seen and trapped from time to time and are always worth looking for in especially cold winters. It is often thought that stoats become ermine as a means of camouflage against a white background and while this is a useful device it is not the sole reason. Many ermine are seen in conditions where there is no snow, and the usual brown colouration is often seen in snowy conditions – in either case the effect of camouflage is completely lost. Whiteness in animals during winter is more a function of temperature than the amount of snow on the ground. Examination of a mammal hair under a microscope will show that it is a hollow tube filled with pigment cells which give a particular colour depending on what the pigment is. The hair of a winter-white animal will be seen to be completely devoid of any pigment and is therefore just a hollow tube with little or no colour. A coat of hollow tubes has much the same effect as double glazing and provides superb insulation, keeping the animal warm. In some areas the weasel will turn white also, but this is much rarer and requires almost arctic conditions. White weasels are virtually unheard of in the West Country, as are the white mountain hares.

Moorland covered in unspoilt snow can be one of the most rewarding places to visit during a cold spell. The whiteness gives an extra dimension to the hills

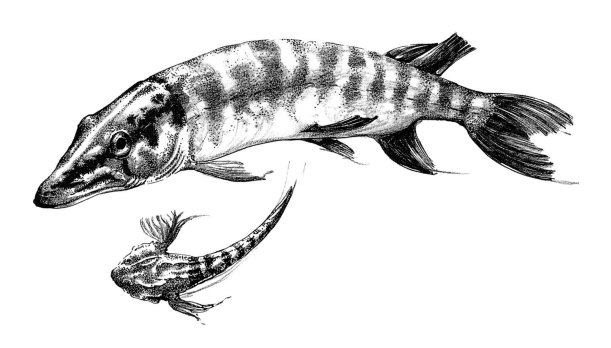

and valleys and seems to increase their contrast. A hilly landscape takes on the grandeur of some of the more mountainous regions of the world when covered with snow, and moorland in winter, whether it be Dartmoor, Exmoor or Bodmin Moor, provides some of the most breathtaking scenery in the West Country. The babbling moorland streams move no more but are stilled by the freezing effect of cold. Huge tracts of virgin snow remind one of the icefields of the north and, like them, can cloak dangers beneath. The sun low in the sky is ideal for bringing animal tracks into relief and at this time of day you can be confident that all indentations have been made by nature. The open spaces means you can follows trails for miles and it is there that a whole night's activity can unfold with every step. Moorland does not hold a vast number of mammal species but snow on the ground can give you a vivid idea of just how busy nature can be. Rabbits should be easy enough to spot and where there are rabbits there are always foxes. A lonely, clitter-strewn tor may well provide the only cover for a fox's earth within miles and backtracking will reveal where it is. A bit more trim than the print of a dog, the fox tracks will sooner or later lead you to where it has found food. Scratched-up snow around pony or cattle droppings show where it has looked for beetles or grubs. If woodland is close by but droppings are not, look for the tell-tale tunnel of a vole or shrew, secure in its elongated igloo until the fox finds it. Fox tracks will inevitably meet those of a rabbit or a grouse and a change of direction will be seen as the predator locks on to its prey. Tracks may run parallel for quite a distance but the outcome seems unavoidable and all that is left as evidence of the drama are a few feathers or bits of fur and perhaps some crimson spots of blood on the otherwise pure snow. Footprints leaving a tumble of rocks on the moor should always be closely examined for the fox is not the only medium-sized mammal which is found out in the frozen wastes. The badger, too, will occasionally find a living, especially around the edges of moorland. The footprints of this animal are unmistakable, its broad strong feet, five-toed and armed with stout claws for digging, leave prints which cannot be confused with those of any other creature.

With some mammals in hibernation and others eking out a meagre existence it is perhaps surprising that others are going about the business of breeding and rearing their young. Eerie, bloodcurdling cries in the middle of the night, around about Christmas time must have given rise to the many stories of nocturnal demons that walk the moors and even enter villages and towns. Foxes mate but once a year and December is the time they choose to do so, and they do it very noisily. Winter chill seems to sharpen the senses and the lack of a deadening cloak of leaves on the trees in the woodlands ensures that sounds carry further than usual. During January one of the sounds you are likely to hear in most woodlands, but especially in Devon, is the mating call of the grey squirrel. A receptive female probably attracts her suitors by smell and all the males downwind will start to make their way towards her. The first male on the scene approaches her in a series of stiff jerks with his fluffy tail proudly spread

• *Pike and bullhead from a North Devon river*

and held over his body to show off to the greatest effect. Chattering loudly and slapping the branch with his front feet he moves closer until she is so overcome with his advances that she makes off in the other direction. A real chase develops as he heads off in hot pursuit, over branch, up trunk and from one tree to another. Heedless of anything else the chase continues pell mell, the commotion giving any other males something to target in on and they may join in the chase

132   • *Winter landscape near Yes Tor, Dartmoor*

as well. After a frenetic session the female will choose her champion and encourage him to approach, all the time chattering. The young are born later in February and raised in the leafy nests called dreys.

The coastline of Devon and Cornwall can be thought of as a thin and delicate ribbon between sea and land. Here nature seems not to have quite made up her mind what to do; sometimes the ribbon is exposed as land while at others it is

Exmoor Pony

Parmelia Lichen

Cladonia Lichens

Wind-pruned Hawthorn

Logan Stone - Rough Tor

submerged beneath the waves. The battle between the two elements is constant and at one time of the day the sea seems to have triumphed, at another she is vanquished. The nature of the coast varies throughout the day, at different times of the month and with the seasons. Different types of rock and the strength of waves and currents help to shape the beach; what we see today can change dramatically tomorrow and the seashore is probably the most dynamic habitat we have. The differing aspects of the coastline and the diversity of geology provide, in the West Country, a variety of different types of beach, each with its own populations of plants and animals, and each a source of discovery for the naturalist. Even on a single stretch of beach conditions can vary within just a few feet, with differences even more profound when you travel from beach to beach and county to county. Beaches of the same type will almost certainly share similar species of animals and plants but no two beaches are identical – there is always something new to see and discover. Despite being one of the most accessible of habitats, beaches are still at the 'edge of Neptune's kingdom', a kingdom full of surprises. Many strange and wonderful creatures come to rest at the water's edge. With a careful eye and an enquiring mind it is still possible to ask questions which have no known answer and find animals which are rare or unknown in British waters.

Among the different types of beach the pebble and shingle beaches are perhaps the least rewarding for the naturalist. The grinding action of the wave-borne pebbles makes short work of any creature which is unfortunate enough to find itself stranded there. Sandy and muddy beaches are, at first sight, not very promising. Vast swathes of apparently barren land are presented to the eye and it often takes a careful observer and a lot of digging to expose the life which waits patiently beneath the surface to be liberated once more by the waves at the next tide. Sands and muds are in fact among the most productive of beaches, but they are unfortunately also the least accessible for the casual visitor. Much more rewarding are the stretches of the coast where cliff meets sea and rockpools are formed. It is here that the battle between land and sea reaches its height and the battle between both is also fought with the changing weather. Each day the tide ebbs and flows twice, now exposing the life of the shore and then submerging it within a few hours. The amount of time a particular organism is exposed or submerged depends on exactly whereabouts on the shore it is. The further away from the sea, the longer the exposure; the lower down the shore the more time spent under water. At the highest part of the beach only those organisms which can withstand prolonged periods out of the sea can survive, and these are almost land creatures. At the very edge of the lowest tides the water seldom disappears completely and the creatures which inhabit this zone of the beach are to be regarded first and foremost as sea creatures. Between the two extremes a gradient forms along which each creature will have its place. Life at the shoreline is not just a question of being exposed or submerged. As the tide recedes, so the drying effect of the sun and

• *Logan stone below Rough Tor, Bodmin*

wind plays a part. Water trapped in rockpools will gradually evaporate and the remaining water becomes more salty. Rain provides an influx of fresh rainwater and may dilute the rockpool to brackish, if not fresh, conditions. When the sea finally returns it becomes salty once more.

Terrestrial and marine life merge, the one trying to colonise the sea, the other staking a claim on the land. Each organism involved in this grim battle is at the very edge of evolution, as well as the tide, and each is perfectly adapted for the life it leads. But each has its place on the shore, and the beach is zoned from the cliffs to the water, each band holding its particular plants and animals.

Rock-pooling is traditionally a summer pastime, but the nature of the sea is such that it is interesting whatever the season. There is no better way of spending a few hours on a bright winter's day than investigating the rockpools. The solitude more than compensates for the coldness of the water, itself soon forgotten as discovery after discovery is made. The more protected rocky shores of the south coast of the West Country are perhaps the most productive but the Atlantic-washed north coast has its own character and inhabitants. The beaches near Ladram, Torquay, Prawle Point, Wembury and Coombe Martin in Devon, and Bude, Trevose, Land's End, The Lizard and much of the south coast of Cornwall as well as the creeks along the the Carrick Roads, such as near St Just-in-Roseland, are also of interest.

To appreciate fully the diversity of life along the seashore the time of the spring tides is best (lows are always conveniently around midday in the West Country). With your back to the land, follow the tide as it recedes, but do watch out for the incoming tide. At the top of the beach where the tide seldom reaches and only salt spray has an effect, the flotsam and jetsam of the sea is cast up and here you will find those land livers which have chosen to risk the highest tides and freak waves as they eke out an existence. It is here that the real changeover from land to sea dwellers is most apparent. Gulls jostle for position with crows and starlings along this thin line, as they all turn over the debris from the deep in search of prey. At night shrews hunt for invertebrates while fox and rat scavenge amongst the sea's cast-off bounty. Among the invertebrates are some creatures specialised to endure the odd ducking. *Ligia oceanica*, the sea slater, can be found here. Skulking beneath stones and in crevices during the day these, Britain's largest woodlice, are denizens of the dusk, and at about 2.5 cm long they are beautifully camouflaged against the rocks. The beach-living bristle-tail is also to be found here – *Petrobius maritima*, a seashore 'silverfish'. Although insects are perhaps the most versatile of all creatures and have managed to exploit almost every habitat, from the tops of mountains to the bottom of lakes the one environment which has beaten them is the sea. It is true that some insects are able to float on the surface skin of the sea, the surface tension, and make a living by scavenging or pouncing on other insects unfortunate enough to be trapped by water, but no insects have been able to become fully aquatic in the marine environment.

ROCKPOOLS

The animals which inhabit rockpools are highly adaptable and cope with an ever-changing habitat. Submerged for part of the day, then exposed and salt-concentrated by the sun, they may then be diluted by rain. It should come as no surprise, therefore, that even in winter pools hold a wealth of creatures. Pipefish lay among the weeds which keep them moist; cushion stars lurk in the damp atmosphere beneath boulders, and the fragile brittle stars are often to be found among the holdfasts of kelp or secreted within an empty shell. As the tide recedes the tiny, blue springtails emerge from their crevices to scavenge upon upon the dead and decaying flotsam left behind by the tide.

Pipe Fish

Sea Lettuce

Starfish

Springtails on Limpet

The tiny springtail, *Anurida maritima*, is the nearest that there is to a marine insect. Scavenging at low tide among the rocks, these blue-coloured insects are at first difficult to see, but any dead or dying sea snail will attract all of the springtails nearby and an upturned limpet soon becomes cloacked in a velvety-blue covering of these insects. Such small insects are obviously at risk from being washed away but can float quite happily on the surface of the water where they may be seen in wind-drifted rafts in the rockpools. When the tide returns to cover their feeding grounds they do not migrate back up the beach but hide themselves into small crevices among the rocks. A hand lens will reveal that they are covered with fine, velvety pile-like hair which traps a bubble of air in much the same way as some water beetles. If by chance one of these springtails nearby and an upturned limpet soon becomes cloaked in a velvety-it will last it for three days – one breath every third day is therefore a very useful adaptation for a life at the water's edge.

While drowning might not be a problem for those creatures which can be regarded as marine, the waves still hold a threat. At the water's edge the crashing tumult of the water carries tremendous strength. Many animals and plants are placed on the shore at just the right place to withstand the waves that occur there but even so conditions at the seashore can be unpredictable and they are all at risk from being dislodged or destroyed. A variety of habits have been developed which keep this danger to a minimum. Some creatures, like the bread crumb sponge and the star ascidian take on a body shape quite different to that of the same animals living in deeper, calmer waters. Offshore both animals grow in a very free way and will become pendulous with many outgrowths. At the water's edge such an outline would produce resistance to waves and would probably result in the animals becoming fragmented. These animals have assumed a flat outline for seashore life and grow on the sides of boulders on the lower shore. A hand lens will be necessary to see the detail of the 'sea mats', which also encrust rocks as well as some of the more substantial seaweeds. What appears to be a white sheet will be seen to be made up of a series of 'windows', each of which houses an individual animal. Like the star ascidian and the sponge, the 'sea mat' is a colonial animal, the neighbouring individuals sharing the same supporting stucture. In the case of the star ascidian it is each petal of the 'star' that is an individual. Shared living is taken to the extreme with all in the star sharing the same mouth.

Beautiful in itself, the star ascidian is often an indicator of one of our most attractive sea snails – the cowrie. In many parts of the world cowries are esteemed for the attractiveness of their shells which have given them a value and led to their being collected in vast and threatening numbers. The little cowries of the British coast are not so large nor may they be so beautiful of shell, but they are still among the most attractive of molluscs, especially when the animal is still alive. Cowries are often found on the undersides of boulders at the lowest of low tides. They are worth looking for if you have found the star ascidian, the cowries' favourite food. When high and dry the sensitive body is completely withdrawn into the shell. It is when the tide returns, or one is placed in a pool, however, that the true colours can be seen. Gradually the body extends from within its delicately ribbed, porcelain container and spreads upwards and over the shell. The lemon yellow 'foot' and orange 'head' are now seen at their best and represent nature at her most artistic.

For the molluscs life is not easy; a large shell is protective for most of the time, but against the buffeting of the waves it can be a distinct disadvantage. A look at the shells of the shore-living snails shows that they are very sturdy and thick. Often, as in the netted dog whelks and sting winkles extra strength is provided by ribbing, producing sculpted shells which, though smaller, are equally as beautiful as the more exotic species favoured by collectors. All of these shells can withstand a certain amount of rolling in the surf, but it is far better to be able to remain in one place and the animal which has perfected the art of staying where it wants is the limpet. The limpets which adorn the rocks are amongst the commonest animals along some seashores. Their stout, conical shells provide the perfect home for creatures which are buffeted by the incoming waves and endure long periods of exposure to the desiccating air when the tide recedes. If

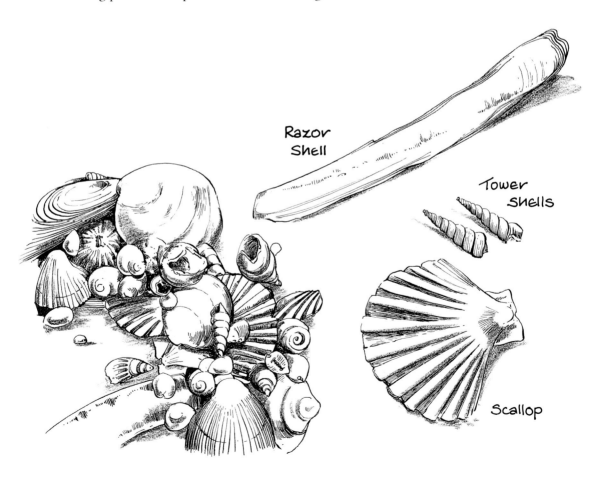

Razor
Shell

Tower
Shells

Scallop

you have ever tried to remove a limpet you will soon realise that the more you try the stronger becomes the mollusc's hold on the rock; this is exactly what happens when the crashing waves attempt to dislodge it. The wide base gives the maximum area of attachment to the sucker-like foot of the snail while the cone shape gives least resistance to the water.

All shore animals face the danger of drying out when exposed above the water line, but the firm grip of the limpet ensures that a reservoir of sea water is enclosed within the shell, providing its own personal ocean from which it can obtain all the oxygen it needs to survive until the life-giving sea returns and covers it once more. A beautifully shaped shell and an often irregular surface to the rock would at first sight make a bad match and the limpet may grind down the rock to fit the shell or work the edge of the shell to fit the rock. Most limpets combine these two techniques to achieve a perfect seal. In soft rocks and with an ever-growing limpet the grinding action may be a constant chore and a limpet scar, often very deep, will result. This scar is home to the limpet; during feeding it will browse on the algae growing nearby but will always return to this same spot, literally a niche which it has carved out for itself. I remember well dislodging limpets and marking them so that the individuals could be identified. A similar mark was made alongside each limpet home and the animals removed to a short distance away. After a period of time varying up to a couple of days, and depending on how far from home the limpets were taken, they all returned to the spots from which they had been dislodged. This homing instinct of the limpet is well known but might not seem as spectacular as the journeys of birds or salmon. It is, to my mind, equally amazing. They must find their way back by 'tasting' the water and tracking in on the smell of their own little patch. With rocks appearing like mountains to them, gullies like huge ravines and ever-swirling waters it would be a bit like us trying to get across Dartmoor in a gale with only our noses to guide us (a remarkable, if not impossible, feat).

The desiccating heat of the sun is a peril which all seashore creatures must overcome. The further up the shore a creature lives the less time it is submerged and the more serious the problem becomes. Many creatures, like the limpets, trap their own bit of sea within the framework of their bodies. At the top of the shore the barnacles close their 'doors' and wait for the next tide. The anemones are also zoned, depending on their ability to withstand exposure.

All of the sea anemones are animals, not plants as their name might suggest, and are armed with stinging tentacles. Each tentacle has myriads of tiny barbed, poison-bearing harpoons. The tentacles are the means by which these sluggish animals catch their prey of fish and crustaceans. The tentacles are stretched and moved by means of water pressure within the animal itself and so water is very important to it. Some are more capable of conserving water than others.

Actinia equina, the beadlet anemone, is common on the middle shore where it appears as amorphous blobs of green, red or brown jelly, quite unlike the delicate open 'flower' it becomes in the water. As water levels drop the tentacles are withdrawn and locked safely away in the body to wait for the next tide. This is achieved by a circular muscle around the base of the tentacles. One form is attractive even when closed – the strawberry form which is flecked all over with 'pips', hence the name. Further down the shore the amazing 'snakelocks' rarely withdraws its green, pink-tipped tentacles and is seldom found outside a pool which will hold water until the next tidal influx. Further down the shore and even less likely to be caught out with not enough water is the incredible and aptly named dahlia anemone. Like many species of anemone, the dahlia anemone is very variable in its pattern and colours and no two will be exactly the same, thus providing the perfect 'flower' border to nature's own 'rock gardens' beneath the water.

Not all of the animals will be exposed to the elements at low tide and many of them will actually follow the receding tide out. Others find a hiding place away from the glare of the sun and the hungry mouths of predators. Beneath weeds and under rocks are obvious places and you would do well to begin a seashore search here. The underside of any substantial rock conceals a wealth of life. Many crustaceans find sanctuary beneath stones and under weeds as the tide falls. Athough it may appear that their tough outer shells will prevent water loss, the shells are jointed and water can evaporate from these joints, so these creatures are as prone to desiccation as any other. Crabs are among the most obvious denizens of the seashore, and looking in deep crannies or under overhanging rocks will soon reveal specimens of the edible crab. More common is the shore crab, perhaps the best adapted of the crabs for life on the shore. At different stages of its life history it may change its colour and pattern as a response to its surroundings. Young crabs are often brightly coloured with distinctive patterns which help them merge into the gravel at the bottom of pools. As crabs grow they tend to move into deeper water and live among weed and so they take on an overall greenish tinge; real deep-water crabs, where the light from the sun is filtered, appear brownish as a reaction to the dominant red colour at these depths.

Most adult crabs seek deeper water in the winter and it is at this time, especially in the West Country, when the females can be seen to be carrying their eggs; some of these 'berried' females will be found on the shore. Males select a female just before she moults and they carry her around while the mating is taking place. Pairs of crabs are often found locked in an embrace during the autumn, the male holding the female below him as he walks. Once mating has taken place the eggs are not released into the plankton but are carefully placed beneath the female's tail, which is broader than the male's for this purpose. The eggs appear as an orangey mass of granules, having the texture of soft brown sugar. The female takes great care of these eggs, making sure that each is well supplied with clean, oxygen-bearing water. At this time she is at her most aggressive in an attempt to protect her offspring.

A careful search of the shore may reveal crabs which are parasitised by the parasitic barnacle *Sacculina*. Unlike most barnacles this species does not have a shell but gains its protection from living within the crab's body, beneath the tail. When the barnacle becomes gravid, its egg mass takes the same position as the crab's eggs would normally but it is of a much smoother texture than the granular egg mass of its host. The presence of this parasite causes the female crab to think that she is carrying eggs and she does all that she would normally do to keep the eggs clean and well. Males are just as prone to infestation as females but not only does the male begin to act as if he were female he also adopts all of the maternal care exhibited by a female in 'berry'.

The strikingly marked velvet swimming crab is the largest and most aggressive crab of the seashore. The carapace is covered with fine hairs which give it a rough-velvet texture; the legs are brightly streaked with blues and red at the joints; while the eyes are bright red, giving this crab a demonic look which is very much in keeping with its aggressive temperament. Careful searching will reveal some of the smaller species such as the broad-clawed porcelain crab and the hairy crab. The broad-clawed porcelain crab clings tenaciously to the underside of rocks where it filters its food from the sea water. These flat crabs can be found in great quantities on various parts of the beach and as many as thirty individuals can be found on the lower surface of a single, quite small, rock.

Two crab-like creatures may also be found in reasonable quantities: the beautiful squat lobster which with a flick of its tail will jump back into the water, and the hermit crabs which take over the cast-off shells of molluscs. Hermit crab watching is a pleasant pastime and half an hour by a rockpool can provide fascinating entertainment. It might, at first sight, seem foolhardy to give up a swift moving and heavily armoured body, after it has taken nature millions of years of evolution to perfect it, but this is just what the hermit crabs have done. Their nearest relatives on the seashore are the squat lobsters, whose defence is to get out of harm's way by shooting backwards like their much larger namesakes. The hermit crab, on the other hand, withdraws into its shell to be rolled where the tide takes it, and while this method of defence might appear rather random it is very effective. One robust claw serves to block the shell opening and the animal can take as much disturbance and receive as much protection as the original inhabitant of the shell. Since hermit crabs are squatters in other animals' shells they have no means of increasing the dimensions of their adopted homes but they grow and moult like most other crustaceans and soon find living conditions so cramped that they have to look for a new, larger home.

I once collected half a dozen hermit crabs of various sizes, and placed them in a tank full of empty shells, including some very large common whelk shells. Faced with such an abundance they scurried back and forth until each settled on a shell which seemed to suit. Claws and antennae were used as probes to test each shell's suitability but the crabs would not be rushed; a careful investigation lasted many minutes before the ideal home was chosen. Moving in was much faster, with the curled, soft abdomen being quickly extracted from the old and inserted into the new home. Like a house-buying chain a queue soon developed with smaller hermits waiting for the ones further up the chain to vacate before they could move in, their own shells going to the next in line. Occasionally a crab would change its mind and decide that its original home was better than the new one, only to find that while it was off house hunting another squatter had moved in. Possession seemed to be nine-tenths of the law and although minor fights occurred the new owner usually stayed in residence. All of them aspired to the 'big house on the hill' and investigated the too-large whelk shells as if to say 'one day that will be mine'; and in some cases they took home ownership very seriously and established a small territory around themselves. One dominant hermit became the master of all he surveyed, perched at the top of a large rock where he could detect all comers. Occasionally when an invader clambered slowly up the shear edge of this fortress to make a challenge the sitting tenant would begin to vibrate from side to side, a signal to give up and leave. Often this worked, but on one occasion the agitation of the tenant became so great that he shook himself right off the rock, leaving the way clear for the usurper.

Some hermits are very happy to share their homes with other animals as long as they are not of the same species. Most obvious are the sea anemones which grow or are 'planted' on the surface of the shell. Doubtless the anemone benefits from scavenging the hermit's leftovers while the crab itself is afforded some protection by the stinging tentacles of the anemone.

Where water has been trapped the ghost-like convoys of the delicate shrimps are first detected by their shadows as they move jerkily in formation in search of food. A stray human shadow sends them scurrying for shelter but patience will be rewarded when they return to investigate the weeds and rocks for fragments of food, their antennae and fine forceps-like pincers moving in all directions, testing their environment.

The water-filled pools are the enforced homes of a variety of fish. Some of these may have been trapped by the tide and so you can expect to find almost any species. Among the most exotic looking are the wrasses; these are brightly coloured fish whose males positively vibrate with colour during the breeding season. Young individuals are often trapped by the tide.

There are many species of fish which actually live on the shore or close to it and spend low tide hidden, and often out of water. The moisture left beneath rocks and weed is quite sufficient for their survival. Finding some of these requires some practice as they are superbly camouflaged in the weedy sanctuary. The pipe fish, as its name might imply, is long and thin and usually of a greenish/brown colour, looking for all the world like the thong weeds among which it hunts when the tide is up and hides when it is down. Two species are

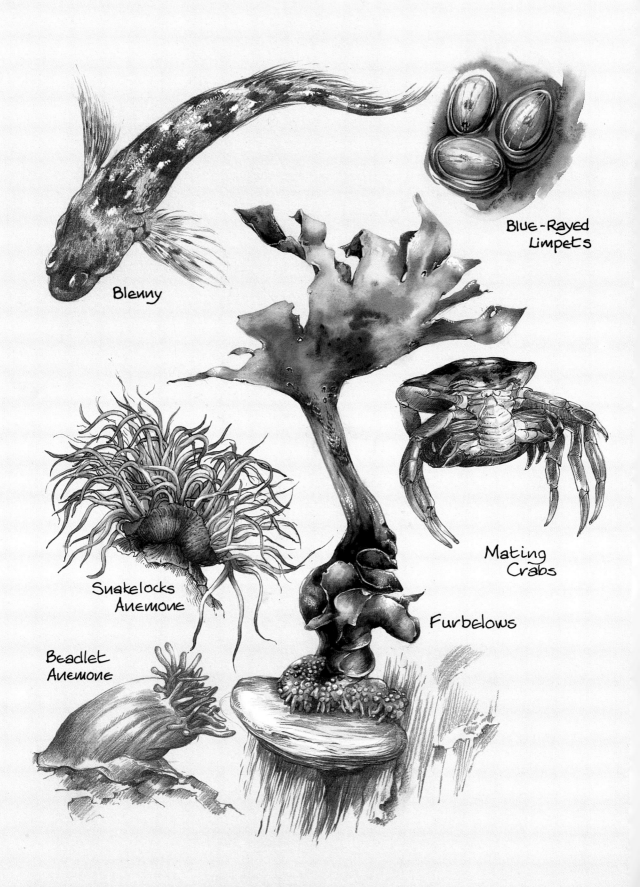

Blenny

Blue-Rayed
Limpets

Snakelocks
Anemone

Mating
Crabs

Beadlet
Anemone

Furbelows

most likely to be seen – the greater pipefish and the worm pipefish. The latter breeds through most of the summer and autumn and you may be lucky during the earliest part of the winter to find the eggs. Unlike most fish the eggs are carried until they hatch and even more surprisingly it is the male that develops a brood pouch and takes on the 'maternal' duties. A cylindrical brownish fish looking rather like a straightened out sea horse with a series of small orange 'ball bearings' on the underside is most likely to be the worm pipefish. This habit is shared with its cousin the sea horse, which, if you are exceptionally lucky you might find as well for they have been taken in coastal waters in the last few years. The long shape of these fish is ideal protection in the swaying fronds of the seaweeds when the tide is in. The butterfish takes protective colour a stage further and has a pattern of spots along its snake-like body which break up its outline, making it very difficult to see. The peculiar dark-coloured bearded rocklings are also well worth looking for but they are difficult to spot as coloration provides them with perfect camouflage.

Another obvious feature of shore life is the crashing waves which at every turn threaten to dislodge any creature on the shore and carry it out to sea. Many of the fish which live under this threat are specially adapted to prevent such an event happening. Their shape is streamlined to allow water to flow over with the least possible resistance; some of them also show remarkable adaptations of the fins to form suckers that help in maintaining their attachments to the rocks.

Easily spotted when it moves, the common blenny is less obvious when at rest for its colours blend perfectly with the encrusting algae of the pool bottom. Hidden under stones at low tide, the blenny is capable of living quite high up on the shore. This fish is perhaps one of the best adapted to life in the rockpool for it will eat almost anything it can get its sharp teeth into and will even wait poised above a seemingly impenetrable barnacle until the creature kicks its legs into the water in search of its own prey. Quick as lightning the blenny strikes, biting off the net-like legs of its prey. The blenny itself is prey to larger animals and an examination of the pellets cast by marauding seabirds will often show the bones of this fish. The most amazing fish of this part of the coast is the Cornish sucker or clingfish. As its name implies, it tends to be more numerous in the south of the West Country and I have yet to find it north of Hope's Nose on the south coast. With a scaleless skin and smooth, flattened shape it offers little resistance to the currents which wash over it and its sucker, which consists of a circle of the pelvic and pectoral fins, is so strong that once the fish has a grip on stones, or even your finger, it is difficult to dislodge. Like many of the fish of the shore it has a mottled appearance, but it can be quite orange in colour and always has two prominent blue 'eye' markings on the upper side. It is a comical-looking fish with its duck-like beak and inane smile but it survives admirably in an environment which is so harsh. Much remains to be learned about even the simplest life activities of this fish and a few minutes spent watching it might reveal something of interest, previously unknown.

• *Species from a rockpool, Prawle*

Unlike the sea, where conditions remain pretty stable and the changing seasons are not so pronounced, life on land reacts to the shorter days and colder temperatures. Perhaps the most noticeable changes are among the birds. The bare fields and leafless trees ensure that any birds that are around are easily seen and during the winter months when territorial disputes break down and food becomes scarce many 'birds of a feather flock together'. Starling flocks are some of the most spectacular and many towns and cities will have their own invasions each evening as the sun goes down. As dusk approaches feeding stops and small flocks make their way to the evening roost. The flocks furthest from the roost site rise first and, flying in a straight line, they are joined by more and more birds until in a locust-like swarm they form a huge flock which contains thousands of birds, wheeling and turning but seldom colliding. When the roost is close the birds circle and stoop, as if one creature, now landing, then taking off again. This is no silent descent for their clamour can be heard as they argue about which way to go and which is the best site. Where the roost consists of a few trees the starlings crowd in as if the trees had suddenly got their leaves back. The roost flight takes place at the last possible minute to allow for the maximum feeding period during the day, but still giving time to reach the site before darkness. Roost sites attract the attention of predators as well and it is not unusual to see an opportunist sparrowhawk or even a pair of tawny owls, one flushing birds and the other catching them.

Many birds roost communally but one of the most amusing is the wren. Normally a tough and vociferous little bird which will not allow any others in its area, the wren becomes remarkably friendly during the winter nights. The cave-like nest of the wren might suddenly become open house for all the wrens in the neighbourhood, and since the wren is regarded as our most common bird this can amount to quite a lot along the hedgerows. One by one the wrens make their mouse-like way along ivy-clad walls to the secret rendezvous and squeeze into the nest along with any others which might have got to the party earlier. Nest boxes are also well used by wrens in winter and there is one record of 50 in a single box. In country districts within the West Country thatched roofs have been used for roosting; wrens are small birds and can lose their heat very quickly, so being packed in together is a way of keeping warm. Not surprisingly another of the tiny British birds does the same thing. Long-tailed tits cuddle up together until all that can be seen is a fluffy ball of feathers with just the tails sticking out. The precious little bodies which do not have enough fat reserves to get them through a very cold night warm each other up in the comfort of their very own communal duvet. During the day 'bottle birds' move about in family parties of a dozen or so birds. Their black, white and brown plumage and constant twittering are a delight as they pass through the woods, flitting from bough to bough. Daytime flocking has great survival potential for the birds concerned and all differences are put to one side when the weather poses the greatest threat to life. An individual starling descending on

HOLLY AND IVY

The verdant foliage of holly, ivy and mistletoe make a welcome addition to the otherwise drab countryside of winter. The almost magical appearance of greenery has led to these plants being surrounded by much myth and legend and before they became an obligatory part of Christmas they were revered by the druids as a sign that life would be renewed when the cold of winter was replaced with the first breath of spring. Of the three mistletoe is the most parasitic, relying for at least the raw materials of its food from the tree upon which it grows: its green leaves, like those of other plants, convert the food by photosynthesis. Legend has it that prior to the Crucifixion the mistletoe was a tall forest tree but because its wood was used for the cross it was relegated to the diminutive parasite we see today. Ivy, while gaining support from trees, does not gain any food from them and is thus not truly parasitic, although its encircling stems can cause distortion of growth of its host. The thick leathery and waxy leaves of ivy and holly are an adaptation to cold conditions when water is difficult to obtain and the cold winds remove moisture from normal leaves quickly. Mistletoe berries are a valuable source of food for many birds and both holly and ivy provide food and shelter for a wealth of wildlife at the raw end of the year.

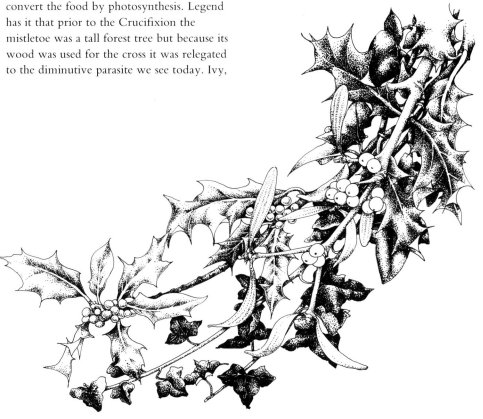

farmland to feed spends as much time looking around as it does feeding and so is not as efficient as it could be. The more starlings that join it the less time it needs to keep its eyes open for danger and the more it can concentrate on the basic task of obtaining enough food. If by chance a stray sparrowhawk drops down the chances are that it will be seen by at least one bird, and even if not then the more birds there are for it to choose from the less likely it is that any single bird is the target. Group feeding, therefore, has distinct advantages, but starlings are well known for their irritable natures and squabbles are constantly breaking out. When feeding on farmland there is normally plenty of food and plenty of space

• *Leverhuses Rocks near St Just*

and each bird has its own personal but mobile territory, keeping its distance from its neighbours. Every now and again one bird will step into the space of another bird and arguments break out. In artificial feeding situations such as are found on bird tables all of the food is in a small area and each bird wants to claim it so the inevitable squabbles take place.

Agricultural land can be a real lifesaver in winter as there is always some stubble and fallen grain to be found and so the seed eaters get together in mixed flocks. Chaffinch, linnet, goldfinch, redpoll and siskins may fly together and feed together rising as a cloud when you have noticed them and have come too

close. A real West Country speciality bird is the cirl bunting with over 90 per cent of Britain's population spending the winter on farmland in Devon, and a good proportion of that number taking over a few fields along the coast near Prawle Point. In woodlands mixed flocks of tits wander from tree to tree and in the conifer plantations goldcrest may join them in the search for food. Some of the largest winter flocks are those of the redwing and fieldfare which can amount to hundreds of individuals in one flock. Driven from the colder Scandinavian countries these birds arrive in autumn but it is in the winter months when they can best be appreciated. The redwing is the smallest British thrush and its high-pitched call and rusty flanks should identify it immediately. The fieldfare could be mistaken for the resident mistle thrush but its colours are more striking, with a slate-coloured head and rump and chestnut back and distinctive clacking call. Both of these thrushes move into gardens as the icy grip of winter takes hold, and when snow covers the frozen ground they appear in large flocks by the roadsides. Roadside verges are both a godsend and a threat to the fieldfare and redwing for they remain unfrozen as a result of the enormous quantities of salt spread to keep ice from the road surface. Much of this spills over the sides and defrosts the vegetation, keeping the ground soft enough for probing bills. The disadvantage is that the flocks are easily startled and I have seen twenty birds dead as a result of collision with cars, in almost as many feet of road. The carnage throughout the region and the rest of Britain must be enormous at these times. Likewise roadside ditches provide good places for the long-billed snipe, another common sight along our dual carriageways during the winter months. The rounded wings, floppy flight and 'peewit' call should leave no doubt as to the identity of the sharp-crested lapwing flocks which strut nervously over the winter ploughed fields.

While some of the inland flocks are quite large they fall very short of the spectacle which can be witnessed on our estuaries during the winter. In the West Country the word estuary is used to describe a number of habitats which, strictly speaking, do not fall within the biological or geographical definition of the word. Some of them are really drowned valleys or 'rias', a result of sea level rises after the retreat of the last Ice Age. They are often steep-sided and lack the extensive mudflats of the estuaries proper. Nevertheless low tide still exposes intertidal areas which can be crawling with birds and most of them have a system of creeks which provide secluded havens for waterfowl and waders. Wherever a river meets the sea the conditions which are produced by the admixture of salt and fresh water, mud and sand are ideal for a variety of plants and animals living on that changeable area between submersion and emersion.

Starting in East Devon the Axe and Otter are small estuaries which do not harbour the largest of populations but their compact nature makes life easier for the birdwatcher. The Exe is the most important estuary in the area and further down the coast that of the Teign, the Plym and the Tamar are well known to birdwatchers. The drowned valleys of the Kingsbridge Estuary and the Dart

A tributary joins the River Camel at Little Petherick, near Padstow •

are more like inlets of the sea than true estuaries, but are well known birdwatching sites. Around Plymouth there are the minor estuaries of the Avon, Erme and Yealm and the complex which includes the Plym, Tavy and Tamar. This massive area of tidal flats is shared with Cornwall and is the place where the important River Lynher outpours. Further along the south coast of Cornwall are the Fowey and Fal, the latter being one of the great birdwatching sites in the county, not least because it opens inland into the vast tracts of water known as the Carrick Roads from which numerous creeks run inland. The Helford River reaches the sea through one of the most beautiful wooded valleys in Cornwall where water and woodland birds can be seen in close proximity. Although not quite an estuary, the fresh-water marshes at Marazion are regarded by many as the finest birdwatching site in Cornwall. Just across the neck of land which separates off the Land's End peninsula is the Hayle Estuary recognised by the RSPB as being of immense importance. The Camel and Amble Rivers come together in the Camel Estuary, the last significant site along the Cornish Coast. Between Bideford and Barnstaple on the north Devon coast the confluence of the Rivers Torridge and Taw forms an extensive system of estuary muds, marshes and sand dunes and is second only to the Exe.

The larger estuaries are obviously more productive as far as quantity of birds and variety is concerned but the smaller estuaries should not be neglected.

EXE ESTUARY

Estuaries large and small dot the Devon and Cornwall coastline and act as a magnet for wildfowl, waders and birdwatchers during the winter months. The red-billed, black and white oyster catcher is usually resident throughout the year, but its numbers are swelled into thousands by visitors from further north. Each day brings new arrivals and departures and the birdwatcher should always be on the lookout for the rarities among the wheeling flocks, which may just pop in for a few days or weeks on their way elsewhere. Being at the southern tip of the British Isles makes the estuaries of the West Country all the more important as stopping-off places for birds which rely on the vagaries of the tides for roosting and feeding sites, each species in its allotted place, searching for its specialist food.

Many a rarity has dropped in to even the smallest inlet because it provides the conditions the bird requires. The smaller estuaries have the advantage of grouping the birds closer together and quite often closer to the watcher. Some, like the Avon, are easily approached by car and have special interest for the less mobile visitor.

Of all the West Country estuaries the Exe is the jewel in the crown. It is one of those wildlife sites which has almost every conservation designation that can be awarded. It is a Site of Special Scientific Interest, Wildfowl Refuge, EEC Conservation Area, and Ramsar Convention designated wetland site.

Of interest throughout the year the Exe Estuary is a special attraction to thousands of birdwatchers during the winter when its resident populations of waders and waterfowl are boosted by migrants which come to spend the cold dark days of winter in a locality which is less harsh then their breeding grounds further north up to the Arctic. At its height 20,000 waders and hundreds of ducks and geese eke out an existence in the mosaic of habitats which are collectively known as the Exe Estuary. Saltmarshes and sand banks, mud flats and water meadows, and mussel beds and open water provide a variety of feeding and roosting places for these massed visitors. Estuaries can be thought of as the transport cafes of the bird world. Some birds stay and others drop in to refuel before travelling further south. On those clear days in winter when the tide is low and the birds are moving in to feed, the air is full of movement reminding one of an international airport. Air traffic control is almost perfect as the birds find their approach altitudes and directions. Air misses are frequent, however, as one flight of birds swerves to avoid collision with another before coming to land on its chosen 'runway'.

When the tide is in an estuary just looks like grey water and at low tide it appears to be a vast area of uninviting mud, but the numbers of birds, if nothing else, reflect the productivity of this 'barren' waste. A scoop of rich estuarine mud is alive with tiny invertebrates, thousands and thousands per cubic metre. Like a motorway cafe the food is laid out in a particular order and the various birds know where to go. Different substrates and proportions of salt and fresh water support different invetebrates and plants and it is to specific areas that the different species of bird go. A walk around an estuary will show that the relationship of the bird to its feeding can be quite defined and that certain birds will only be found at certain parts of the estuary. The whole complex is like a giant jigsaw, each piece a raft of hope and nourishment to the birds concerned. The hinterland of any estuary is as important as the tracts of mud and water for when the tide is in many of the birds will resort to land for roosting and feeding. Wet meadows are especially important, providing soft ground for probing wader bills. Birdwatchers can gain the most reward in the shortest time as the tide is rising, and the birds move up the beaches towards the waiting binoculars.

Sanderlings, as their name might imply, are often to be seen where a sandy shore is exposed. Trotting along the tide line these graceful grey waders look almost clockwork in their movements. Where seaweeds are cast up the turnstone is almost always to be found flicking over the algal fronds in search of the rich harvest of invertebrates. Redshank and the less common greenshank may be joined by the occasional spotted redshank on the saltmarshes. On the lower estuary the plump knot can be seen running away from an incoming ripple and then turning to follow it out, probing the ground as it goes. Its name is supposed to be an imitation of the grunting sound it makes but the *canutus* part of its Latin name reminds one of King Canute who tried to keep the tide at bay. Two species of godwit can be seen in their hundreds on the Exe Estuary. They can both be seen almost anywhere but the bar-tailed is more likely to be seen at the lower end of the sandbanks whereas the black-tailed frequents the upper reaches and surrounding farmland. The Exe Estuary is internationally important for this bird and during the winter may be home to 17 per cent of the north European population. Both godwits have a slightly upturned bill and therefore cannot be confused with the similarly coloured curlew. Next to the warbling cry of the redshank the call of the curlew is the most distinctive sound

• *Shag on the rocky shore at Erme Mouth, South Devon*

of a winter estuary at night. Many of the waders are restricted to feeding when the tide is low and so they cannot always afford to wait until low tide and daylight coincide. This means that they have to visit the mudflats during the hours of darkness when the food is available. The curlew is only one of two waders on estuaries with a noticeably down-curved bill. The smaller whimbrel is not found here during the winter months and so the squadrons of large brown waders with bent beaks are almost certainly curlew. The length of leg and especially the bill show that the birds sharing an estuary are not all eating the same foods and are thus not in direct competition; the longer-billed birds exploiting those animals which live deeper in the mud such as ragworm, the shorter billed birds turning over debris in search of invertebrates hiding beneath them or probing the surface muds for the tiny hydrobia snail.

It is fitting that the Exe Estuary, where the Royal Society for the Protection of Birds is so active, should be the site for the largest flock of avocets in the West Country since this bird features as the organisation's logo. They are very specialised feeders and so are quite restricted in their distribution to those few

places within the estuary where salt and fresh water mix in the correct proportion to support the opossum shrimp, a favourite food of the avocet. The specialism is helped by the unique upturned bill of the avocet which it swishes from side to side in the water to filter out its food. The most comfortable way of seeing these birds is also the best way and that is to take one of the 'Avocet Cruises' organised each year by the RSPB. Most of the estuary birds have learned to live with slow-moving boats and many such cruises take place on the larger estuaries. The avocet with its curved bill, stilt-like legs and black and white plumage is immediately recognisable as one of the most elegant birds of the estuary. Another black and white bird which is found feeding along the mussel beds and can be seen roosting in huge numbers, all facing into the wind and many standing on a single red leg, is the oyster catcher. Despite their name they feed mainly on mussels in the Exe and a close look at the bill may show whether they are a 'chiseller' or a 'hammerer' when it comes to opening the tough shells. The long orange bill cannot be confused with any other bird and the piping call and white bands along the wings when it is in flight makes the oyster catcher one of the most noticeable birds of the estuary.

Some wildfowl are resident throughout the year on the West Country estuaries but the inclement weather in the frozen north causes many species and thousands of individuals to make the journey south to these havens. As far as the Exe is concerned the wigeon and brent geese are among the more obvious visitors; 5000 of the former and almost as many of the latter come to the estuary. When these birds occur in such large numbers it is difficult to imagine that they are regarded as being in need of protection, but the huge rafts of them reflect the security and good feeding in the Exe. Both populations which winter here are recognized as being of international importance. The brent goose is nothing like as frequent in Cornwall but the wigeon can be seen in relatively large numbers at St John's Lake near Torpoint, around the Tamar Estuary and on the Camel Estuary. Both of these species begin arriving in September and gradually more arrive until the mid-winter peaks are reached around December.

The handsome teal, the black, white and brown shelduck and the ubiquitous mallard are all easily spotted among the crowds but there is always the chance of some of the more uncommon species, such as pintail, eider, goldeneye and gadwall. Among the geese the large black-necked and bar-headed Canada goose is very noticeable, either on water or grazing among estuarine marshes. This is a species which, once an uncommon visitor, has been introduced onto lakes in the region as a decorative bird and has taken to life in the wild extremely well so that it can now be seen almost everywhere there is water. Sometimes consorting with the flocks of Canadas are barnacle geese, a smaller species which has the front and sides of its face white, and is thus easily distinguished from its larger cousin. Grey lags, white fronts, pink foots and other species are all worth looking out for. The sleek sawbills are especially welcome and the more open areas of water are the best places to see them. The

Merganser in a reed bed near Slapton •

red-breasted merganser is a regular visitor to the larger estuaries and the Carrick Roads complex of channels and creeks.

The merganser's similar–looking relative the goosander is more likely to be seen inland on the larger rivers, reservoirs and the few stretches of natural open water. Dozmary Pool near to Bodmin's highest point at Brown Willey, is one such lake, and, indeed, the only one of its kind in Cornwall. Otherwise unprepossessing it is well worth the short walk from the road in winter, just in case an interesting bird has turned up. Surrounded by bleak moorland , it is a

• *Lundy coast in January*

natural landmark for any wildfowl flying over and, as such, has an attraction out of proportion to its actual suitability for a number of species. The goosander has already been mentioned and the mallard is to be expected; the lovely black and white smew, long tails, goldeneyes and the charming tufted duck also occasionally put in an appearance while the rusty-coloured pochards seem to like this environment and are there most of the time.

Large concentrations of any bird species act as a magnet for the predators and a sudden start will send the flocks wheeling in all directions as a hungry

peregrine stoops in to pick off a straggler or cold-weakened bird. Any disturbance might mean the proximity of a predator but continual heckling of a bush or tree is likely to point to the presence of one of the species of owls which inhabit the West Country. In a garden or park it is likely to be the tawny owl, trying to ignore the small birds which refuse to let it sleep through the day until it has moved out of their feeding area. Among coastal scrub, sand dunes and on heathland the bird is likely to be the short-eared owl, itself a visitor from points north. Usually seen close to the ground, the short-eared owl is looking for small mammals, although it may take the odd small bird, and relies on its eyes rather than its short ears for locating its prey. The 'ears' are tufts of feathers and serve no purpose when it comes to hearing, although they are used for communication and body language within the species and as part of threat displays.

The sea coast, and particularly the headlands which jut out into the sea, are well known as seabird watching points and can be rewarding places to visit in all weathers. The continual passage of birds as they migrate locally between feeding grounds can be a wonderful sight, as can watching the sea-loving divers, grebes and sea ducks such as scoters. After a gale the shore and nearby inland are welcome refuges for some of those birds which spend much of the winter out at sea; guillemots, little auk and storm and fork-tailed petrel may all be encountered along much of the coast.

FIELD NOTES

NATURE
RESERVES
AND AREAS OF INTEREST

M ost of the prime sites in the two counties of Devon and Cornwall are designated Nature Reserves. This confers some protection to the sites in question. Some nature reserves and other sites are so sensitive as to be regarded as off limits to the general public while others are difficult of access, so both of these categories have been omitted from the following list. Many organisations now hold land in trust and confer some protection on the wildlife it contains. The two county Trusts for Nature Conservation, the Royal Society for the Protection of Birds, English Nature, the National Trust, the Woodland Trust, and County and District Councils all play their part in conservation. Not every site can be detailed so the list here is a very select one. The status of nature reserves changes from time to time and the number of reserves, fortunately, is always increasing; for more information it is always best to contact the organisation responsible for running the particular reserve. A 'Reserves Handbook' is available from the Cornwall Trust for Nature Conservation and a set of 'Reserves Cards' from the Devon Wildlife Trust.

In order to maintain interest on a site or encourage further diversity most nature reserves are managed to some degree. This might at first sight sometimes seem dramatic and destructive, but management plans are formulated from the best information available at the time for the site in question. Information on species present, especially for many invertebrate groups, is still incomplete for many reserves. You can help by informing the relevant organisation of the animals and plants you discover on your visit:

Devon Wildlife Trust, 188 Sidwell Street,
Exeter, Devon EX4 6RD.

Cornwall Trust for Nature Conservation,
'Five Acres', Allet, Truro, Cornwall TR4 9DJ

English Nature (formerly Nature Conservancy Council) (SW Region – Cornwall), Trelissick Feock, Truro, Cornwall TR3 6QL

• *Avocets are a welcome sight on the Exe Estuary*

163

English Nature (formerly Nature Conservancy Council) (SW Region – Devon), Old Mill House, 37 North Street, Okehampton, Devon EX20 1AR

Royal Society for the Protection of Birds,
10 Richmond Road, Exeter, Devon EX4 4JA

The Reserves are in alphabetical order of name within each county, followed by the Ordnance Survey grid reference. In addition to these specific sites there are many country walks and 'nature trails' which it has been impossible to mention. It is sometimes regarded as counter-productive to mention special sites, as if the rest of the countryside was of lesser value. It should be remembered at all times that these sites are only those which have been designated or are protected in some other way; many other sites merit protection and deserve respect when you visit them. Fences and gates are there for a purpose and footpaths are marked for everybody's convenience; use them, but do not abuse them. Never take samples of plants or animals unless you have written permission from the correct authority. Do not disturb nesting birds or other animals with young, and bear in mind that you are only a guest in the countryside – leave it as you have found it.

It is not the intention of this book to include a sketch map of every Nature Reserve, Site of Special Scientific Interest or locality mentioned in the text, indeed the two counties are so rich in 'wild places' that it would be impossible to do so within the space available. We have, however, chosen to highlight a few of those which we particularly enjoyed visiting while compiling this book. They may be especially interesting from a birdwatching point of view, they may exhibit a rich flora or they may just please us scenically. Any other two people might choose completely different areas to illustrate and our selection reflects our own tastes.

CORNWALL

BISSOE VALLEY
(SW 773 413)
3 hectares, former derelict mine site, with ponds, grassland and newly planted woodland.

BRENEY COMMON
(SX 054 610)
55 hectares of wet woodland, scrub, heath, bog and ponds. Birds, lepidoptera, aquatic.

CARN MOOR
(SW795 538)
1 hectare wet heath.

CRACKINGTON HAVEN
(SX 143 968)
Especially interesting for the much contorted rocks and land slips which inhibit the growth of oak woodland resulting in stunted trees within the National Trust

Reserve at Dizzard Point.
Clifftop grasslands and heathland,
and grey seal offshore.

DEVICHOYS
(SW 775 381)
16 hectares of ancient woodland.

DOWNHILL MEADOW
(SW 863 689)
1.6 hectares of dry meadow and
wet heath.

DOZMARY POOL
(SX 195 745)
One of the very few natural
stretches of water in the West
Country. The pond is set in a
shallow depression within the
granite and is a natural attractant
for small numbers of water fowl,
especially during the winter
months.

FAL-RUAN ESTUARY
Trelonk (SW 890 405)
Ardevora (SW 881 406)
100 hectares of tidal mud flats and
salt marshes. Birds.

GOLITHA NATIONAL NATURE RESERVE
(SX 227 690)
18 hectares broadleaved woodland
on River Fowey. Especially important
for mosses, lichens and woodland
birds.

HAWKES WOOD
(SW 986 709)
3.6 hectares ancient woodland.

HAYLE ESTUARY
(SW 5437)
200 hectares of mudflats, sand and
salt marsh, with extensive dune
systems. Migrant wildfowl and
waders in winter.
RSPB reserve.

KEMYL CREASE
(SW 460 244)
2.4 hectares conifer plantation on
old bulb fields.

KENNAL VALE
(SW 750 374)
8 hectares broadleaved plantation
with some ancient woodland.

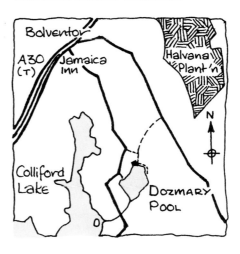

LEVERHUSES ROCKS
(SW 394 306)
Much of the Land's End Peninsula
is covered by coastal moorland
and grasslands. The cliffs and
sea stacks provide a home
for large numbers of breeding
seabirds. Grey seal are
regularly to be seen offshore,
especially in the autumn.

THE LIZARD
(SW 7118)
A unique collection of rock types
and a mild climate have led to
the formation of an interesting
collection of vegetation. Much of
The Lizard Peninsula is National
Nature Reserve (which is managed
by English Nature), a reflection
of its very special character.

LOVENY/COLLIFORD
RESERVOIR
(SX 184 744)
132 hectares moorland reservoir.
The largest stretch of open water
in the county. Wildfowl in winter.

LUCKETT
(SX 392 728)
4 hectares of woodland. Flora,
birds, butterflies.

NANSMELLYN MARSH
(SW 762 543)
4.5 hectares of reed bed and
willow carr. The keys to the bird
hide can be obtained from the
CTNC.

NORTH PREDANNACK
DOWNS
(SW 688 174)
40 hectares of Lizard heathland.
Botanical.

PARK HOSKYN,
THE HAYMAN RESERVE
(SW 748 497)
1.8 hectares mixed broadleaved
woodland.

PELYN WOOD
(SX 088 588)
40 hectares mixed broadleaved
wood. Botanical.

PENDARVES WOOD
(SW 641 377)
16.5 hectares broadleaved/conifer woodland with lake.

PERRAN MEADOWS
(SW 774 382)
3.2 hectares wet meadow crossed by River Kennal.

PETER'S WOOD
(SX 113 910)
10 hectares ancient, coastal valley oak coppice.

PHILLIP'S POINT
(SS 199 043)
2 hectares clifftop maritime grassland and heath.

PORTHCOTHAN VALLEY
(SW 868 713)
6.5 hectares unimproved meadow, scrub and wet woodland.

REDLAKE COTTAGE MEADOWS
(SX 126 592)
13.8 hectares on unimproved damp meadow and wet heath.

RED MOOR
(SX 070 622)
24 hectares of wet woodland, scrub, bog, heath and lakes.

ROCHE ROCK
(SW 991 596)
On the edge of 'china clay country', Roche Rock provides a superb vantage point for the surrounding countryside with its damp heath vegetation

ROPEHAVEN CLIFFS
(SX 034 490)
20 hectares of cliffs and broadleaved woods. Birds.

ROUGH TOR
(SX 195 745)
A typical tor on the Bodmin Granite. One of the highest points in Cornwall, Brown Willy, at 1375 feet (c. 420 metres), is also marked on the map. Both are excellent vantage points for viewing the surrounding Bodmin Moor.

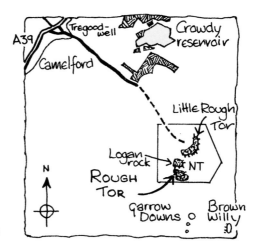

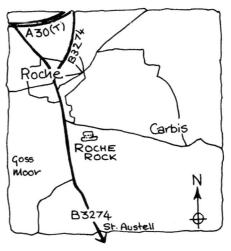

RUMPS FORT
(SW 934 812)

Ideal vantage point for seabirds and grey seal. The Camel Estuary is one of the more important in Cornwall and it is especially interesting during the winter months when the resident population of birds is joined by migrant waders and wildfowl

TAMAR ESTUARY
(SX 432 630)

400 hectares of tidal mudflats and salt marshes. Birds.

TINCOMBE
(SX 417 589)

0.6 hectares, urban wet meadow.

TREMELLING
(SW 550 340)

2.4 hectares wet mixed broadleaved woodland with marsh plants.

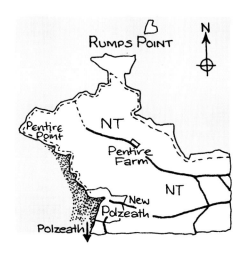

UPTON MEADOW
(SS 207 044)

8 hectares dry unimproved meadow and scrub.

VENTONGIMPS MOOR
(SW 781 512)

8 hectares of wet mixed broadleaved woodland, ponds, wet and dry heaths.

DEVON

ANDREW'S WOOD
(SX 707 515)

23 hectares woodland, grassland. Invertebrates especially butterflies, glow worm. Birds. Largest colony of heath lobelia in the country.

ASHCULM TURBARY
(ST 147 157)

6.5 hectares wet heath, bog, wet woodland. Bog plants, dragonflies. Reptiles and amphibians.

AXMOUTH TO LYME REGIS UNDERCLIFFS
(SY 253 900-SY 329 916)

About six miles of ash-dominated woodland along the delightful East Devon/Dorset coast. The area is very rich in most kinds of birds and not forgetting the spectacular geology and fossils. Occasional glimpses of the sea are to be had through the dense woodland cover. Walkers are strongly advised to keep

to the marked paths as the terrain
can be difficult and dangerous
elsewhere.

AYLESBEARE COMMON
(SY 057 898)
182 hectares heathland. Birds,
lepidoptera, botanical.
RSPB reserve.

BLACKADON
(SX 714733)
37 hectares sessile oak woodland.
Ferns. Birds.

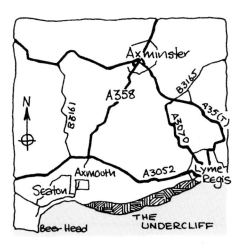

BRAUNTON BURROWS
(SS 4437)
The most extensive dune system
in the West Country. Especially
interesting for its spring and
summer flowers and its butterflies
and birds. A variety of dune
habitats provide a wealth of
choice for the naturalist of any
persuasion. English Nature
reserve.

BROWNSHAM
(SS 287 257)
30 hectares wet and dry heath,
grassland, woodland, stream.
Butterflies, wet pasture flora.

BUZZARDS WITHLEIGH
(SS 910 166)
A typical Devon river-valley
woodland of coppiced oak on
either side of the Little Dart
River. This National Trust
Reserve comprises over 30
hectares and includes water
meadows. It is especially
interesting in spring.

BYSTOCK POOLS
(SY 034 844)
20 hectares woodland, heathland, ponds, reservoir. Butterflies, dragonflies, reptiles, amphibians. Permit required.

CAIRN
(SS 515 463)
7.7 hectares woodland, old railway. Flora, invertebrates, birds.

CHAPEL WOOD
(SS 483 413)
5.7 hectares RSPB reserve.

CHUDLEIGH KNIGHTON HEATH
(SX 837 776)
54 hectares wet and dry heath. Plants, invertebrates, birds.

DART VALLEY
(SX 680 727)
360 hectares old coppice. Ferns, mosses, lichens, invertebrates, birds.

DUNSFORD
(SX 798 875)
57 hectares woodland. Wild daffodil, dragonflies, butterflies, birds.

EXE ESTUARY
(SX 975 845)
The most important estuarine site in the West Country which now enjoys a series of national and international wildlife protection initiatives. It is of particular interest for its huge wintering populations of waders and wildfowl, some of which are internationally significant. Mud and sand flats and adjoining marshes ensure an ornithological interest at all phases of the tide. Dawlish Warren, with its dune plants, adds to its value.

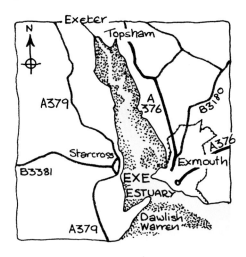

EXE REED BEDS
(SX 957 885)
25 hectares reed beds. Birds.

EXMINSTER MARSHES
(SX 958 875)
Low-lying wet grassland, reed beds, ditches. Birds. RSPB reserve.

FROWARD POINT
(SX 905 497)
23 hectares pine woods, scrub, cliff grassland. Birds.

THE GRANGE
(SX 897 500)
11 hectares pine/oak/beech woodland, grassland. Plants, birds.

HALSDON
(SS 555 125)
57 hectares river, woods, marsh, meadow. Plants, mammals, birds.

HALWILL JUNCTION
(SS 443 004)
2.4 hectares. Grassland, heath and scrub. Birds, butterflies and plants.

HANGINGCLIFF WOOD
(SX 428 656)
4.5 hectares woodland, quarry. Redshank, avocet and other estuary birds.

HAWKSWOOD
(SY 201 978)
4 hectares heath, grassland, scrub. Grassland flora, butterflies.

INNER WARREN, DAWLISH
(SX 985 794)
113 hectares mud flats, sand dunes, marsh. Rare plants, estuary/sea birds. Permit required.

LADY'S WOOD
(SX 685 591)
2.8 hectares woodland. Coppice flora, birds, dormice.

LICKHAM COMMON
(ST 127 123)
4 hectares wet heath, scrub. Plants, reptiles, birds.

MELDON
(SX 556 907)
5.6 hectares ungrazed moorland, lake, island. Wet and dry moorland plants. Birds.
Permit required.

MILL BOTTOM
(SX 786 810)
5.6 hectares woodland, railway line. Coppice flora, mammals, birds.

NEW CROSS POND
· (SX 863 737)
11 hectares abandoned clay pit. Plant succession, aquatics, reptiles, amphibians, birds. Permit required.

NORTHAM BURROWS
(SS 4430)
263 hectares sand dunes and shingle ridge. Devon County Council.

THE OLD SLUDGE BEDS
(SX 952 888)
5.3 hectares abandoned filter beds, willow carr. Plant succession. Migrant birds.

OTTER ESTUARY
(SY 076 822)
23 hectares shingle spit, mudflats, salt marsh. Salt marsh zonation, birds.

POSTBRIDGE
(SX 649 789)
Easily accessible and therefore very popular in the summer, Postbridge is the site of one of the 'clapper bridges' for which Dartmoor is famous. To the south

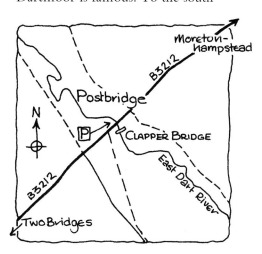

a path takes you to the Bellever Plantations and to the north into open moorland with human settlements of centuries past. In any direction, the boulder-strewn East Dart is a constant companion.

RACKENFORD MOOR
(SS 858 211)
55 hectares Culm grassland. Plants, butterflies.

THE ROUGH
(ST 178 040)
3.6 hectares grassland and flush. Plants, butterflies.

SCANNICLIFT COPSE
(SX 843 860)
7.7 hectares woodland. Oak/ash. Flora. Permit required.

SOURTON QUARRY
(SX 523 897)
8.5 hectares flooded quarry, woodland. Orchids, other plants. Butterflies, birds. Permit required.

STUCKEY FARM
(SS 780 140)
2 hectares Culm Grassland. Flora, butterflies.

SWANPOOL MARSH
(SS 473 367)
2.8 hectares marsh. Flora, dragonflies.

TEIGN VALLEY AND FINGLE BRIDGE
(SX 743 900)
The Teign Valley woodlands are at their best when the spring

flowers are in bloom but at any time of year there is much to see. Dense woodland clothes the steep banks providing homes for many species of bird, insect and mammal. The River Teign itself supports a wealth of invertebrate and fish life which in turn attracts birds such as kingfisher, dipper and grey wagtail and the occasional otter amongst the mammals.

TOD MOOR
(SX 624 541)
7 hectares unimproved pasture, marsh. Plants, birds.

VENN OTTERY
(SY 065 920)
25 hectares wet and dry heath, raised bog, wet woodland. Plants, dragonflies, butterflies, birds, mammals. Permit required.

WARLEIGH POINT
(SX 447 610)
30 hectares woodland, estuary. Plants, invertebrates, birds.

WESTON MOUTH
(SY 163 880)
1.6 hectares wooded coombe, scrub, grassland, landslip, pebble beach. Flora, butterflies, reptiles, birds.

WISTMAN'S WOOD
(SX 613 772)
One of the 'natural' woodlands of Dartmoor. This English Nature Forest Nature Reserve clings to the steeply sloping eastern bank of the West Dart River. It is an 'oasis' of woodland among the stark moorland vegetation and is especially interesting for its stunted oaks a reminder of Dartmoor as it used to be, before forest clearance.

WOLBOROUGH
(SX 864 700)
5 hectares woodland and fen. Pond and grassland nearby. Carr flora, dragonflies, birds.

YARNER WOOD
(SX 7779)
Oak/hazel woodland. English Nature National Nature Reserve.

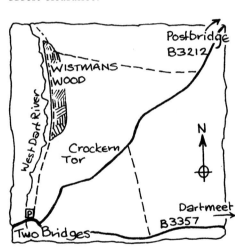

Index

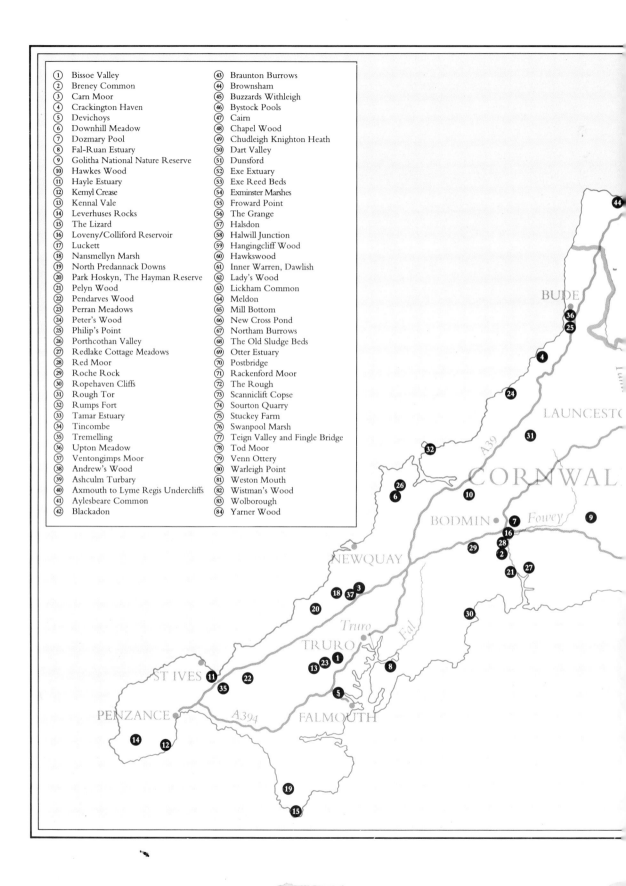

(1)	Bissoe Valley	(43)	Braunton Burrows
(2)	Breney Common	(44)	Brownsham
(3)	Carn Moor	(45)	Buzzards Withleigh
(4)	Crackington Haven	(46)	Bystock Pools
(5)	Devichoys	(47)	Cairn
(6)	Downhill Meadow	(48)	Chapel Wood
(7)	Dozmary Pool	(49)	Chudleigh Knighton Heath
(8)	Fal-Ruan Estuary	(50)	Dart Valley
(9)	Golitha National Nature Reserve	(51)	Dunsford
(10)	Hawkes Wood	(52)	Exe Extuary
(11)	Hayle Estuary	(53)	Exe Reed Beds
(12)	Kemyl Crease	(54)	Exminster Marshes
(13)	Kennal Vale	(55)	Froward Point
(14)	Leverhuses Rocks	(56)	The Grange
(15)	The Lizard	(57)	Halsdon
(16)	Loveny/Colliford Reservoir	(58)	Halwill Junction
(17)	Luckett	(59)	Hangingcliff Wood
(18)	Nansmellyn Marsh	(60)	Hawkswood
(19)	North Predannack Downs	(61)	Inner Warren, Dawlish
(20)	Park Hoskyn, The Hayman Reserve	(62)	Lady's Wood
(21)	Pelyn Wood	(63)	Lickham Common
(22)	Pendarves Wood	(64)	Meldon
(23)	Perran Meadows	(65)	Mill Bottom
(24)	Peter's Wood	(66)	New Cross Pond
(25)	Philip's Point	(67)	Northam Burrows
(26)	Porthcothan Valley	(68)	The Old Sludge Beds
(27)	Redlake Cottage Meadows	(69)	Otter Estuary
(28)	Red Moor	(70)	Postbridge
(29)	Roche Rock	(71)	Rackenford Moor
(30)	Ropehaven Cliffs	(72)	The Rough
(31)	Rough Tor	(73)	Scanniclift Copse
(32)	Rumps Fort	(74)	Sourton Quarry
(33)	Tamar Estuary	(75)	Stuckey Farm
(34)	Tincombe	(76)	Swanpool Marsh
(35)	Tremelling	(77)	Teign Valley and Fingle Bridge
(36)	Upton Meadow	(78)	Tod Moor
(37)	Ventongimps Moor	(79)	Venn Ottery
(38)	Andrew's Wood	(80)	Warleigh Point
(39)	Ashculm Turbary	(81)	Weston Mouth
(40)	Axmouth to Lyme Regis Undercliffs	(82)	Wistman's Wood
(41)	Aylesbeare Common	(83)	Wolborough
(42)	Blackadon	(84)	Yarner Wood

BUDE

LAUNCESTON

CORNWALL

BODMIN • Fowey

NEWQUAY

Truro

TRURO

ST IVES

PENZANCE

A394

FALMOUTH